THE FIRST MAMMALS

THE FIRST MAMMALS

Written and illustrated by

WILLIAM E. SCHEELE

DIRECTOR, CLEVELAND MUSEUM OF NATURAL HISTORY

AUTHOR OF *PREHISTORIC ANIMALS*

THE WORLD PUBLISHING COMPANY

CLEVELAND AND NEW YORK

LIBRARY OF CONGRESS CATALOG CARD NUMBER: 55–8251

FIRST EDITION

ACKNOWLEDGMENTS

To Miss Frances Bungart, Mrs. Alan Gerhardt, Miss Olga Prince, Mrs. Ralph Scheele, and Mrs. Lephe Stockton, I am indebted for their help in typing the manuscript. I am especially grateful to my wife for her help in assembling and typing parts of the rough and finished copy.

cw855

PREFACE

ALL BUT ONE of the animals depicted in this volume are mammals. The species described were selected to stimulate interest in all fossil mammals. Many of these species lived in very recent times, particularly in the period following the melting of the last great glaciers.

This book is intended to be a reference that will stimulate further reading. The span of time covered here is the most recent 60 million years of the earth's history. Men and the apes have been omitted from the text because the story their evolution tells is best separated from that of the other mammals.

In the naming of the species within this volume, some animals are referred to by their most common name, while others carry only the proper scientific name. This lack of uniformity may strike the reader as peculiar, but the names used are those most apt to be encountered by the average reader. Generally the species are arranged within the book according to the appearance of the animals in geologic time. Larger families are covered as a unit so that the important steps in the evolution of the animals within that family can be seen more readily. The vital statistics for each species are presented first in order to provide a résumé of facts such as one would be exposed to in a museum display.

W.E.S.

Modern chipmunks, successful mammals of a type that seems destined to thrive on earth for untold centuries to come

INTRODUCTION

A WIDESPREAD public interest in dinosaurs has focused considerable attention on that particular group of extinct animals. Wherever fossils are displayed, this preformed interest leads those who view the exhibits to overlook the lines of distinction that separate invertebrates from vertebrates, mammals from reptiles, and so on.

Since the science of paleontology is a new one, its goals and formidable vocabulary have not yet become familiar to the public. In geographical areas where fossils are found, people are just beginning to realize that amateur as well as specialist can play an important part in the expansion of this science.

Each group of animals has its own fascinating story to tell. Excavating and preparing any ancient animal for exhibition is a task involving a great deal of time and money. Many private citizens have discovered such animals, and some of them have been permitted to help collect the specimens. Such experiences are always thrilling. In the light of what has happened during the relatively short history of collecting fossil mammals, there are many possibilities of important finds being made by curious people in any walk of life.

The Age of Mammals covers recent times. For this reason alone, specimens that typify these periods are found on the surface of the earth or very close to it. Many of these bones have been exposed by erosion or commercial excavation. Their physical condition is apt to be poor. In addition, the time element is important, because mammal bones are often not old enough to have become petrified as have the bones of more ancient animals. Quick action is usually necessary to preserve the remains of fossil mammals. The scientist, in relying on the public for leads to these fossils, must also rely heavily on the sound judgment of the individual who has the power to dispose of the remains. Ice age mammals, in particular, are likely to be discovered in wet ground, the bone when exposed being soft and swollen. To extract these bones in a hurry is often disastrous. Quick drying and vigorous cleaning will destroy not only the specimen itself but also certain inconspicuous bits of valuable evidence bound to be tossed aside by over-eager excavators.

Many people fail to realize how rich the mammal fauna of North America was ten thousand years ago. Elephants, horses, giant sloths, lions, many kinds of deer, and other mammals abounded in every corner of our country. In places where the land is and was heavily forested, valuable bones are forever lost because decay and severe weather conditions speed up the disintegration of fallen bodies.

In recent times tremendous herds of wild animals have died from drought, fires, and similar causes, but the bones of these animals were not protected from the elements and preserved. Bodies of dead animals must be covered over by earth soon after death if they are to be preserved at all. The best example of this is the scarcity of buffalo bones on the Great Plains of our own West. Years ago these animals were killed by the thousands and left to rot on the open prairie. Today a traveler over these same places would have trouble finding even a scrap of evidence to show that so many animal bodies had once lain there. Weather and scavengers have completely obliterated the remains.

In dealing with extinct mammals, another problem crops up continually. This has to do with the average person's disbelief that any modern-looking mammal bones could be of scientific interest. Animals only recently extinct are often turned up by accident and quickly tossed aside without ever being offered to a museum or school for examination. In our own community, a commercially operated sand pit has produced many fossil species for us. These would never have been preserved at all had it not been for the alertness of a single foreman. His fellow workers had tossed skulls and other bones into the trash can simply because they looked too modern; our friend picked them up to make certain that someone with knowledge could pass judgment on them.

CONTENTS

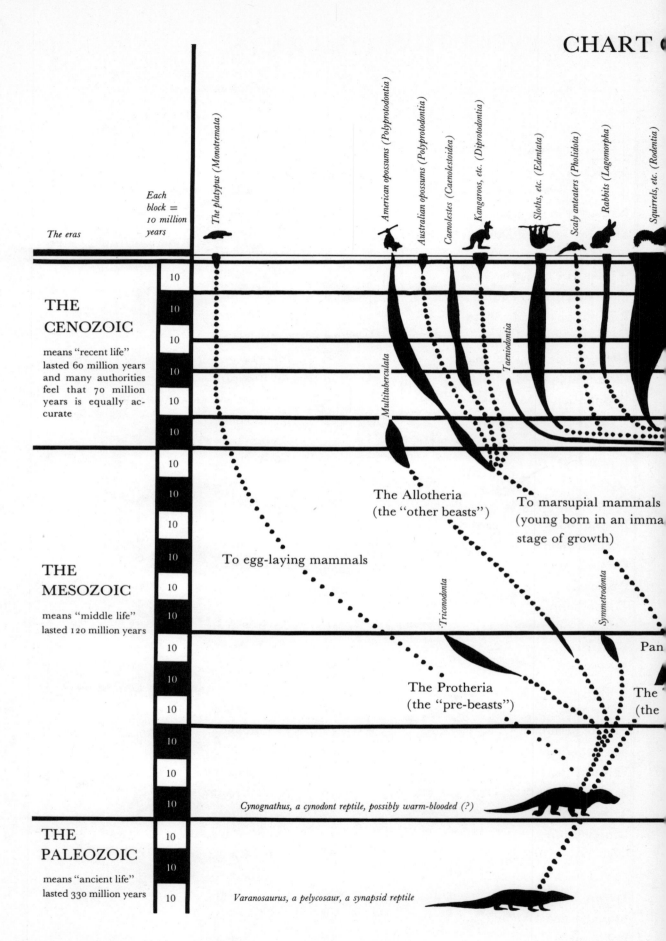

The eras

Each block = 10 million years

The platypus (Monotremata)

American opossums (Polyprotodontia)

Australian opossums (Polyprotodontia)

Caenolestes (Caenolestoidea)

Kangaroos, etc. (Diprotodontia)

Sloths, etc. (Edentata)

Scaly anteaters (Pholidota)

Rabbits (Lagomorpha)

Squirrels, etc. (Rodentia)

THE CENOZOIC

means "recent life" lasted 60 million years and many authorities feel that 70 million years is equally accurate

THE MESOZOIC

means "middle life" lasted 120 million years

THE PALEOZOIC

means "ancient life" lasted 330 million years

Taeniodontia

Multituberculata

The Allotheria (the "other beasts")

To marsupial mammals (young born in an imma stage of growth)

To egg-laying mammals

Triconodonta

Symmetrodonta

Pan

The Protheria (the "pre-beasts")

The (the

Cynognathus, a cynodont reptile, possibly warm-blooded (?)

Varanosaurus, a pelycosaur, a synapsid reptile

8

MAMMAL EVOLUTION

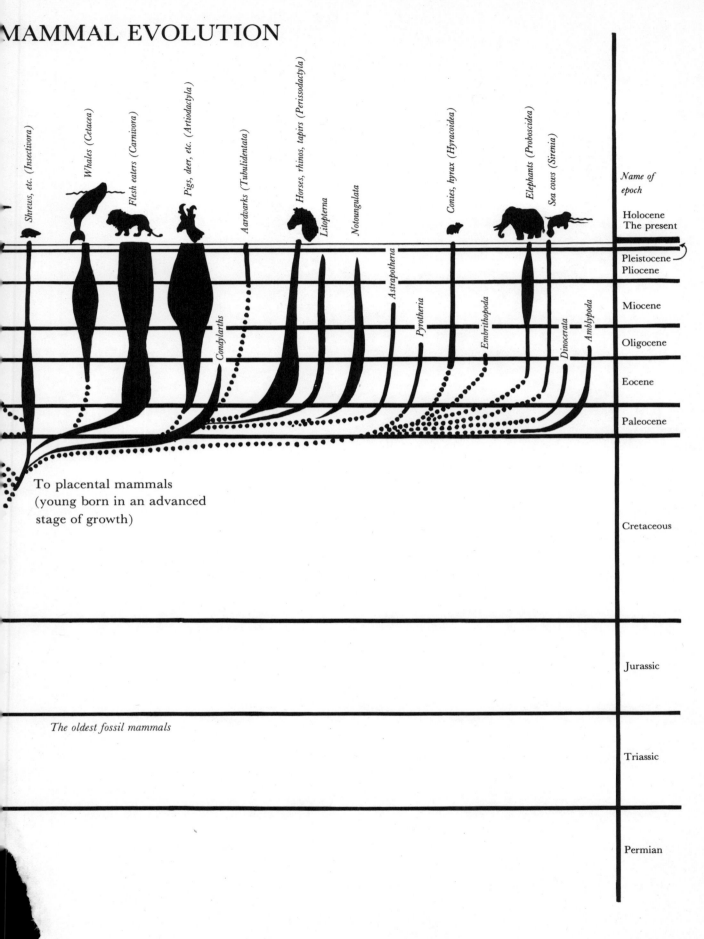

Shrews, etc. (Insectivora)

Whales (Cetacea)

Flesh eaters (Carnivora)

Pigs, deer, etc. (Artiodactyla)

Aardvarks (Tubulidentata)

Horses, rhinos, tapirs (Perissodactyla)

Litopterna

Notoungulata

Astrapotheria

Pyrotheria

Condylarths

Embrithopoda

Conies, hyrax (Hyracoidea)

Elephants (Proboscidea)

Sea cows (Sirenia)

Dinocerata

Amblypoda

Name of epoch

Holocene
The present

Pleistocene
Pliocene

Miocene

Oligocene

Eocene

Paleocene

To placental mammals
(young born in an advanced
stage of growth)

Cretaceous

Jurassic

The oldest fossil mammals

Triassic

Permian

SABER-TOOTHED CATS, SMILODON

WHAT IS
A MAMMAL?

THE WORD "MAMMAL" is confusing to almost everyone. In fact, even some scientists find it difficult to express simply and directly what the word means. Many persons when speaking of "animals" really mean mammals, and the trained zoologist or teacher is apt to be impatient at this lack of distinction between words.

All mammals are animals, but not all animals are mammals. The word "animal" embraces such varied forms of life as insects, fish, reptiles, and other creatures, as well as the mammals. To be a mammal, an animal must breathe air, and it must be warm-blooded. The heart must have four chambers in it. There are other points of internal structure that are quite distinctive, but the basic internal division of the body into two parts, the pleural and abdominal cavities, is characteristic. The young are born alive and are nursed by the mother, except in the case of the monotremes (egg-layers). A body covering of hair is typical, although in some species the amount of hair is reduced to almost nothing.

People often speak of man and the marine mammals, such as the whales, as though they did not belong to this class of living things. Many prefer to use the word "beast" or "quadruped" to designate the four-footed creatures. It took a person of vision to realize that such widely different animals belonged within the same classification. The great classifier Linnaeus (1707–1778) designated the class name *Mammalia,* deriving the word from the Latin *mamma,* which means "teat." Most American texts have adopted the word as "mammal."

Glyptodont, 11 feet long

Living armadillo

Alticamelus, 18 feet tall

Living camel

Giant kangaroo, 10 feet tall

Living kangaroo

African elephant

6 foot hunter

Tallest mammoth, 14 feet

Moeritherium, 3½ feet tall

Zeuglodon, extinct whale, 70 feet long

OMPARATIVE SIZES

All animals drawn to approximately the same scale.
Silhouettes represent prehistoric species; outlined
figures are living species.

ice age lion, 11 feet long

Living lion

Saber-toothed cat, 8½ feet long

*Baluchitherium,
a hornless rhinoceros,
18 feet at the shoulders*

Living rhinoceros

*Living blue whale, a mammal.
The largest animal that has ever
lived. 119 feet is the record length.*

MAMMALS IN GEOLOGIC TIME

FOR FOSSILS of animals that show the first signs of becoming mammals it is necessary to trace back approximately 210 million years into late Permian times, the last of the Paleozoic Era. There are no true mammals to be found here, but there are some reptiles whose bodies and skulls were undergoing a change that most paleontologists feel led to the gradual evolution of the mammals.

In the Mesozoic Era that was to follow, there is a thin thread of evidence tracing through thirty million years of the Triassic Period and into the late Jurassic Period. Here we have the first concrete evidence that mammals were well established and becoming a successful evolutionary trend.

Most of the earliest records of mammals, particularly during Mesozoic times, are in the form of scattered teeth and an occasional tiny jaw fragment. In North America there is only one impor-tant mammal deposit from these ancient periods. This is at Como Bluff in Wyoming.

Entering the Cenozoic Era, the sixty million years in which the animals described in this book are concentrated, there is a very gradual spread of mammals throughout all continents. During the Oligocene Period, there was a vast change in the nature of the world's mammal population. The old and primitive forms died off, and in their place there came into being new and varied animal families, many of which were the forerunners of today's familiar mammals.

Within the history of man there has been a widespread destruction of some mammals. In the very near future we will witness the tragic end of still others. In our own country we have already reached the point where certain mammalian lines can be maintained only in vast government parks. Careful breeding is necessary to preserve them. Some of the wild mammal species classed as big game have been inventoried carefully, and a watch must be kept to see that their numbers do not get below the point that would lead to extinction.

Divisions of Time During The Age of Mammals

NEARLY ALL of the mammals discussed or depicted in this volume come from the Cenozoic Era in geologic time. *Cenozoic* means "recent animal life," and in this span are to be found fossils that can be reconstructed with considerable accuracy.

Geologists divide the Cenozoic into two major periods. The larger, older portion is called the Tertiary, since it is recognized as the third great division of *all* geologic time. The other, the Quaternary Period, includes the recent past and about one million years of the great ice age, the name referring to the fact that this most recent period, in which we live, is the fourth great division of geologic time.

Each of these long periods is further divided into epochs. The most recent times are termed the *Holocene;* this word means "entirely recent." It covers only the past few thousand years, during which there has been great world-wide destruc-tion of mammalian life through the acts of mankind.

The *Pleistocene* Epoch is next oldest; it covered approximately one million years. Translated, this word means "most recent." The epoch is characterized by the tremendous ice sheets that covered a great part of the earth, and by the extinction of older animal forms and the rise of the recent mammals.

The *Pliocene* Epoch occurs next as we go back; it is the latest division of the Tertiary Period and lasted for approximately nine million years. Translated, the word means "more recent." *Miocene* times came next, spanning fifteen million years. Translated, the name means "less recent."

The *Oligocene* Epoch lasted for ten million years; its name means "little of the recent." The *Eocene* was of fifteen million years duration; the word means "dawn of the recent." *Paleocene* times lasted ten million years; the name means "oldest of the recent."

Beyond this point in earth history mammals were relatively scarce, and the land was dominated by dinosaurs.

CHART OF CENOZOIC TIME

The Tertiary Period lasted at least 59 or 60 million years.
The Quaternary Period has lasted 1 to 5 million years.

Abundant animals of the period	Duration in millions of years	Meaning of the epoch names	Epoch names*
Man Rodents Artiodactyls Apes Weasels Elephants Saber-toothed cats Bison Sloths Beavers Bears Wolves	1	"most recent"	Pleistocene
Horses Camels Pigs Deer Rodents Sloths	9	"more recent"	Pliocene
Horses Deer Rhinoceros Glyptodonts Whales Cats Elephants Dogs	15	"less recent"	Miocene
Creodonts Horses Toxodonts Dogs Rhinoceros Cats	10	"little of the recent"	Oligocene
Creodonts Pre-deer Titanotheres Oreodonts Uintatheres Tiny horses	15	"dawn of recent times"	Eocene
Uintatheres Primitive hoofed mammals Creodonts Opossums Condylarths	10	"oldest of the recent"	Paleocene

*An epoch is a subdivision of a period.

15

HUNTING
FOSSIL MAMMALS

DURING the exploration and expansion of western North America, the science of paleontology was given a tremendous boost forward. From the early 1800's until the present time, what are now the western states have been the richest fossil-hunting grounds in the world. The arid and eroded badlands areas have been the greatest source of good specimens.

The first extensive finds of mammal remains in North America came to public attention thirty years after the discovery in 1818 of the first American dinosaur. The initial published description of an important find in the western states was that of a titanothere unearthed in the Dakotas. Fossils from that region were so numerous that by 1852 Joseph Leidy of Philadelphia was able to publish a comprehensive synopsis of all known fossil mammal remains from North America.

President Thomas Jefferson contributed his bit to paleontology by his interest in extinct animals from Big Bone Lick, Kentucky, and other areas in the eastern states. In fact, when the Lewis and Clark expedition departed for the West, they left with instructions from Jefferson to search for living examples of mammoths and other mammals we now know were extinct at the time.

Most fossil mammal displays cannot compete for popularity with those showing the weird anatomical features of fossil reptiles, or the perfection of fish and invertebrate specimens. Though the Age of Mammals has lasted for more than sixty million years, the average museum visitor sees little difference between the skeleton of a thirty-five-million-year-old titanothere and that of a modern rhinoceros. Throughout this country it is typical of museums to display a relatively few complete fossil mammal skeletons, and those only of the best-known extinct animals. Many significant fossil mammals are kept in storage.

The search for remains of extinct mammals differs considerably from the hunt for older fossils. Most mammalian fossils are fairly near the surface of the earth, frequently in unconsolidated stony matrix. Few bones are petrified or protected from weathering by solid rock.

It takes a catastrophe to create good fossils. During the earlier eras of the earth's history there were many changes in the land's surface that trapped and preserved animals singly or by the millions. The vast amount of soil overlaying these dead animals preserved them for millions of years in an undisturbed state. The remains of mammals, though covered by similar later disturbances in nature, were not buried so deeply, and the weather, plant roots, burrowing animals, and other elements have helped to further their disintegration.

Where older fossils often are turned to stone, or protected, more recent bones are exposed or are simply too young to be preserved well and thus need special care when they are found. Those found in dry country require only a coating of a simple toughening agent that will also keep them clean. Bones of ice-age mammals are most frequently found in wet boggy ground; these must be dried carefully and slowly, and then kept from cracking and shrinkage by the use of bakelite or similar material.

There are collecting localities in North America world famous for the abundance and perfection of their specimens. Some of these are worth naming: the La Brea tar pits of California, one of the most amazing fossil deposits of all times; Big Bone Lick, Kentucky; Agate Springs, Nebraska; Peace Creek, Florida; the oreodont and the titanothere beds of South Dakota—to name just a few. Most of the animals described in this book come from these and other North American localities of lesser paleontological importance, and represent a fairly recent portion of Cenozoic time.

Many extinct mammals are known only from very small portions of the total skeleton. Nevertheless, anatomists are able to reconstruct entire bodies from such scraps, because many living species are structurally similar to extinct forms. But, in spite of this ability to recreate forms, it is difficult to trace the ancestry of even the most common type of animal, for key species that show significant change often are known only from single specimens.

This book is but a sampling of the material available. The most familiar animal groups are represented in some detail, while confusing smaller side issues of a main evolutionary line are omitted entirely. Though their bony remains are not too popular with visitors to public museums, the detailed study of extinct mammals is a rewarding one. The proper classification of a species becomes a challenging detective story, for obscure skeletal differences offer subtle clues to its transition toward success in adaptation. Our own success as a race may some day depend to some extent upon how well we learn the lives and past history of our fellow mammals.

Restoration of Body Shape

A KNOWLEDGE of living mammals has demonstrated that it is not always possible to tell by examining its skeleton how an animal looked when it was alive. But many restoration drawings of fossil mammals are more than a guess, for though the first statement is true there are points in a skeleton that offer clues to the animal's external appearance.

Perhaps the most easily restored portion of the body is the head, since the skull and jaws are well knit and of dense bone that preserves well. Teeth are usually found as fossil evidence long after other body parts have disintegrated; they are the hardest part of any animal's body. Teeth are indicative of the living creature's habits: what an animal ate, how it caught its prey, and the manner in which this food was consumed. The location and size of the ears can be readily determined. The size of the eye, the strength of the jaw muscles, the location and size of the nose—all of these points and more

can be traced in the skull. An important clue to the animal's total history is the size and complexity of the brain cavity.

The foot structure tells us how fast and how well the animal could move. The joints of the legs give an indication of the habitat of each animal. The size of the tail bones indicates the strength and the possible use of the tail. In some cases it can be determined whether or not there was long or short hair on the tail. The backbone and ribs tell something of the weight of the animal.

Rough spots on any of the bones tell us of the muscle attachments and the strength of each mammal. Paleontologists cannot reconstruct an entire animal from a single bone, but a single bone can identify an animal.

Yet, if certain modern species were extinct, it would be impossible to reconstruct them accurately from the skeleton alone. The external appearance of the whale and the camel, for example, could not be deduced from their skeletons. The tremendous amount of blubber in certain whales adds considerable bulk to the body, but this is not suggested in the skeleton. There is no clue to the existence of the camel's hump in its skeleton.

These and other reasons could be given for making men wary when restoring extinct forms. However, when direct evidence turns up, scientific restoration proves to have made surprisingly few errors. Quite frequently caves yield mummified animal remains that confirm notions of an animal's appearance. In northern countries, frozen ground often yields the entire fleshy carcass of an animal. Cave paintings and other prehistoric works of art depict still other extinct mammals. All of these help to confirm our conception of ancient life.

The camel's humps do not show in the skeleton

Coloration in Extinct Mammals

It is only by studying living animals that we find reasonable clues to the coloration of extinct species.

The first point to be assumed is that most animals resemble their environment. Among mammals whose ancestry can be traced back through several epochs, the body colors are generally solid and the underparts light colored or whitish. This kind of marking appears to be related to the survival ability of the mammal. It is also apparent that nearly hairless skin is an indication not only of living in the warmer climates, but that the particular animal represents a long established type, and that it very often is a plant eater.

Primitive mammals are believed to have had thick coarse hair, and many of them are thought to have been marked with horizontal stripes. These stripes eventually broke up, evolving into spots; and after millions of years the spots in turn disappeared. The young of certain mammals repeat this protective spotted pattern and offer some support for this notion. Living mammals that have changed very little from their extinct forebears are very often heavily marked with stripes when they are young and carry some of these stripes into adulthood.

There is no known relationship between the skeletal structure and the external body color. The skeletons of a horse and a zebra are almost identical, but they are obviously different animals from the viewpoint of their external markings alone.

Many of the deductions made about the coloration of fossil mammals are based on observation of lower forms of animal life: reptiles, insects, and others. Such comparison may be hazardous, but the ability of the lower animals to reproduce rapidly allows for many interesting controlled experiments in feeding to produce color changes.

Young Malay tapir—primitive body marking

Domestication of Mammals

THERE HAVE been numerous attempts to determine how man first began to domesticate the mammals that are useful to him, but about all that can be said definitely is that the history of man and animals has been closely linked since the late ice age.

Most people agree that the dog was probably the first mammal to become fully domesticated. The remains of fossil dogs are widely distributed throughout the world; many of their bones have been found in situations that suggest they were pets or camp followers, and perhaps useful hunting companions, at an early date.

Formerly, many believed that horses were the next animals to be domesticated, but this notion has now been largely discarded. At present, the theory is widely held that pigs and sheep were penned for use as food at an earlier time than the domestication of horses. These animals, being rather small, were more easily controlled. Pigs were particularly useful around village sites, where they ate refuse and helped keep harmful insects and reptiles under control. The process of domesticating animals that lived in large herds probably began by simply driving a herd into a dead-end valley and then blocking the valley with brush and stones. The captured animals could afterward be butchered when food was needed.

Wild cattle were probably next to be domesticated. This might have taken place in central Europe or in the Mediterranean area, where there were many species of wild oxen. These herds of cattle were numerous, they tolerated man, and they permitted themselves to be corralled and then tamed. The primitive hunters who first realized that the milk of cattle could be used as food discovered one of the important keys to the success of man's own evolution. Without the cow's ability to create milk from grass, none of the earth's populations would have been able to expand and increase as they have. The spread of grasslands over the face of the earth also affected the distribution of man, for pasturage was a vital need in sustaining long migrations and the shift of large population groups dependent on cattle as their principal source of food.

Most domestication of wild mammals has taken place only recently. It was not until a few thousand years ago that man progressed from being a hunter to being a herder to being a farmer and a breeder of specialized animals.

Very little of the domestication process can be learned from fossil remains, but there are a few instances to indicate that live animals were kept as a food supply far back in the dim past of civilization. There have been several recent discoveries that lead authorities to believe that primitive people penned the giant ground sloths, eventually to butcher them. This view is widely debated, since the evidence supporting the idea is slight.

White-tailed fawn

CLASSIFICATION OF MAMMALS

AMONG modern mammals, the color of the hair, the length of an ear, even the color of the eye might conceivably be used in giving a name to a species. In dealing with fossil mammals, such detailed information is obviously not available, and the job of selecting distinctive names becomes difficult. Researchers in this field are often forced to work with remains that are quite fragmentary. This is because the relative age of most fossil mammals is not great, which in turn means that the preservation is not apt to be good. Most often the skull and some of the teeth are the last parts of a body to decompose, and it is these parts that are used most frequently as the basis for description and final classification of fossil mammals.

The study of animal teeth as a major basis for naming and classifying species from any era became more significant after Dr. Edward Drinker Cope (1840–1897) determined that the cheek teeth of mammals evolved from a simple three-cornered molar. Since that time dental formulas for all mammals have been created. These are based on four kinds of teeth: the front teeth, or incisors; the eyeteeth, called canines; the premolars; and the molars, or grinding teeth, themselves. The primitive stock of mammals that seems most likely to have given rise to the multitude of later forms carried a "basic" tooth formula of i 3/3, c 1/1, p 4/4, m 3/3. The double figures refer to the upper and lower jaws, and they represent one half of the total teeth. This formula is multiplied by two, which in this case gives 44. This tooth pattern was quite stable, even though the bodily shape of the several species might be incredibly varied. In man, the dental formula is i 2/2, c 1/1, p 2/2, m 3/3. Multiplied by two, this gives 32, the number of teeth that identifies the normal human being. In contrast to this formula for man, that of the dog is i 3/3, c 1/1, p 4/4, m 2/3. Multiplied by two, this equals 42 teeth. These formulas are unvarying in a species, and the change that occurs over long periods indicates clearly how an animal feeds and what it feeds upon.

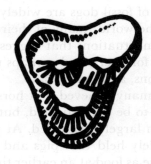

A primitive 3-coned molar tooth

It is obvious that the front teeth would alter and shift as the feeding habits of an animal change. The premolars vary considerably among carnivorous species, and the molars are most helpful in determining the identity of grazing animals. Among grazers, the habit of eating coarse grasses requires that the single cap of enamel on the molar of the typical mammal be replaced by an intricate pattern of folded internal enamel plates that traverse the length of the tooth vertically from crown to roots.

| *Bunodont,* all cones | *Selenodont,* all crescents | *Lophodont,* all crests | *Buno-selenodont* | *Lopho-bunodont* | *Lopho-selenodont* |

VARIOUS MOLAR TOOTH SURFACES AMONG MAMMALS

TYPES OF MAMMAL FEET

Plantigrade foot

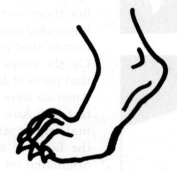

Digitigrade foot

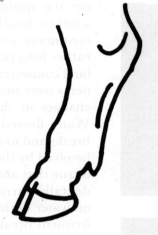

Unguligrade foot

Science has given names to all exposed surface parts of teeth to help in their final definition. Various types of tooth surfaces are pictured opposite, and the diagrams indicate the linking of the name and the specific feature involved.

Another major anatomical feature of an animal that is often used to describe an order is the feet. In this case there is a set of words for each specific appearance and use of the feet. Mammals can be *pentadactyl,* which means "five-toed." This condition is usually found among the most primitive mammals. The foot of a mammal can be *plantigrade,* which means that the entire sole of the foot, or hand, touches the ground. Another descriptive term is *brachypody,* meaning "short-footedness," for example, the elephant's foot. Any combination of these and similar terms grouped together then describe the animal's method of moving, and this method itself typifies large groups of mammals.

For example:

AMBULATORY, slow-moving
CURSORIAL, swift-moving
SALTATORIAL, leaping, swift-moving
FOSSORIAL, digging, slow-moving
NATATORIAL, swimming
ARBOREAL, tree-climbing
GLISSANT, gliding
VOLANT, flying

Wherever possible, descriptions are based on the entire animal skeleton. But, in truth, the number of complete skeletons found is so small that few species can be covered in every detail by such descriptive work. Many important so-called missing links remain to be found. In some cases a long line of evolution within a group of animals is held together by a few pitiful scraps of evidence; perhaps even a single tooth is the only available link.

Many names of fossil mammals end in *-therium* or *-odont. Therium* means "beast," and *odont* means "tooth." The reasons for choosing such names are obvious. But there are also a few mammals that have been named because of an anatomical feature strong enough to suggest a character trait that is more unusual than the skeletal structure. Macrauchenia, for example, is named for its long neck.

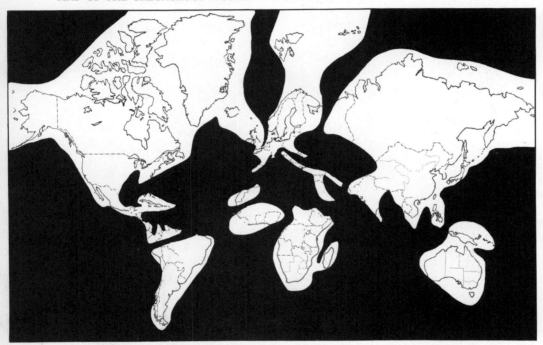

MAP OF THE CRETACEOUS WORLD

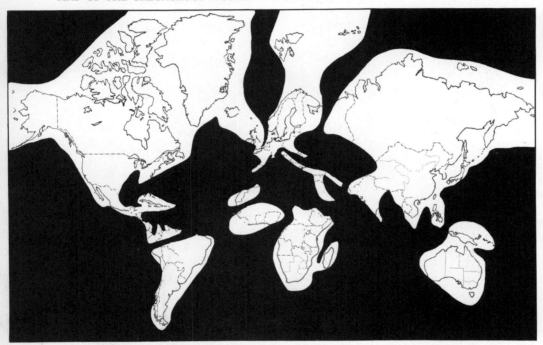

MAP OF THE PALEOCENE WORLD

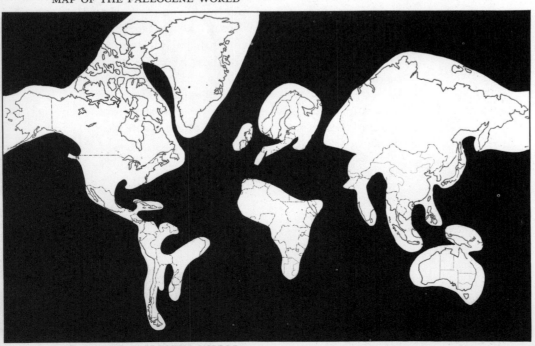

MAP OF THE OLIGOCENE WORLD

Distribution of Mammals

THE SIX world maps shown here represent but one of many versions of the shape of the world's land masses during the Age of Mammals. Within the long periods that each map typifies there were numerous and important minor changes in the terrain that are not illustrated. On the maps it is readily seen that parts of Europe and North America were in prolonged contact with Asia. Students of mammal origins tell us that many of the familiar animals we know originated on the Asiatic mainland and then migrated throughout the world. At one time or another nearly all the major continents were connected for rather long periods. These dry-land connections between continents were broken by structural changes in the earth's surface. Water flowed in to seal off the breaks and to isolate the animals involved by the change. While it is true that animals can be accidentally carried long distances on water during flood times, the frequent breaks in the dry-land connections between continents constitute the prime factor controlling the distribution of mammal species.

Changes of climate can be barriers to the spread of animal populations just as certainly as mountains, forests, and deserts can act as barriers. As the climate of any large area begins to change, there are important changes in the insect population, and these changes in turn are held responsible for the mysterious and complete disappearance of some mammal populations.

One of the important considerations of mammal distribution is the assumption by most authorities that the continents as we know them have been fairly stable for a long time. Opposing this view are those who believe that the continents "float" and were once part of a single large mass of land. Those who hold to the latter theory can cite numerous structural similarities in the continents, which seem to have been sliced apart though they are separated by thousands of miles. The location of some mineral deposits seems to bear this out, and more recently the bones of extinct animals have been brought into the argument to support the theory. A complete knowledge of current paleontological work does not seem to bear out this contention, since for every proof put forth for the continental drift theory there is equal support for the view that the continents have been stable for a long time.

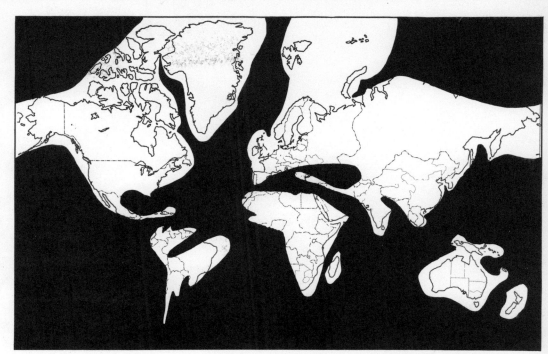

MAP OF THE MIOCENE WORLD

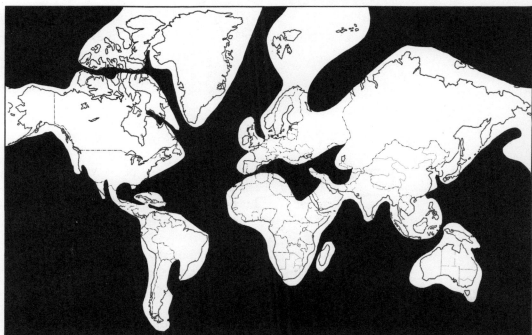

MAP OF THE PLIOCENE WORLD

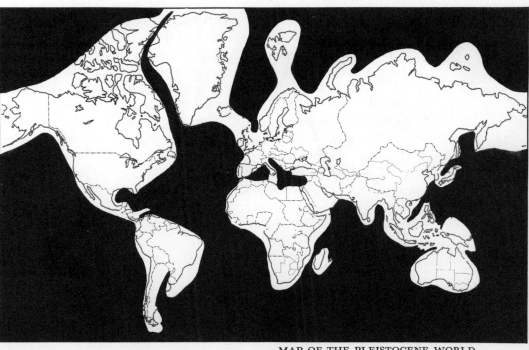

MAP OF THE PLEISTOCENE WORLD

CYNOGNATHUS—*a mammal-like reptile*

Pronounced **sigh · no · *naith* · us**

Translated, the name means "dog-jawed," because of the pattern of tooth placement.

The animal was 5 to 8 feet long.

Lived during Lower Triassic times, 180 million years ago.

Found principally in South African deposits.

Displayed at the American Museum of Natural History in New York City.

IT IS generally conceded that the history of mammalian development begins with this animal and its close relatives. Within the body and skull of the reptile shown here, there are many structural changes that begin to set it aside from the reptiles. Among the things that cannot be determined from the fossil record is definite evidence to back up the conjecture that this animal was one of the first warm-blooded species.

The ancestry of this peculiar reptile group can be traced back many millions of years to Permian times. The Texas red beds have yielded numerous skeletons of a Permian reptile called Varanosaurus. This animal was about five feet long, and in its jaws there are indications of a changing tooth pattern that is continued and developed in Cynognathus. This difference in teeth is a lengthening of the canines and the presence of a sharper tip to all of the other teeth in the jaw. To the paleontologist this means a change of the animal's food habits and thus a more active life in pursuit of quick-moving prey. Both reptiles belong to a group called the therapsids, whose history was well-developed even before the dinosaurs appeared.

In Cynognathus the body was lightly built, but the head was large. The typically reptilian pineal opening (the third eye) had nearly disappeared, and all of the other openings in the skull were changing in shape and location. There was a secondary palate in reptiles for the first time; this permitted the animal to feed the way an active modern carnivore does. The legs were stronger, and they held the body farther away from the ground. The formation of the leg bones shows some modification to permit freer, faster movement over open ground. The gait would have been less awkward.

Related reptiles that were to follow in history increased in size, and their skeletons show many apparently experimental trends that eventually died out, leaving no connection to modern forms. The first successful true mammals, in Jurassic times, were small insectivore types whose relationship to these reptiles is not at all clear.

It is likely that crude, small mammals as yet undiscovered were following a path of evolution parallel to Cynognathus and related species. There must be a fossil series that will link the well-established small Jurassic mammals to the large reptile-mammals thirty million years older.

PTILODUS—*one of the earliest mammals*

Pronounced **till · o · dus**

Translated, the name means "feather-toothed," because of the flat, ribbed, cheek teeth.

The skull was 3 inches long; the body is unknown.

One of the few Jurassic mammals known, about 140 million years old.

Found in Wyoming.

Not displayed, but owned by the Smithsonian Institution in Washington, D.C.

THE SKULL of Ptilodus is one of the rarest fossils. The mammal it represents is one of four very primitive orders that are the only known mammals from the Jurassic Period.

It is supposed that all four mammal groups were probably marsupials (having an abdominal pouch in which the young were carried). Three of them must have eaten primarily insect food, while the fourth, Ptilodus, was a rodentlike plant eater.

The molar teeth of Ptilodus typify a moderately successful group of mammals that lived well into Eocene times. These animals were called multituberculates, because of their tooth structure. The molars were long and narrow; the chewing surface was full of low sharp cusps.

The largest of these distinctive animals grew to be nearly three feet long and must have looked like a modern woodchuck. The group as a whole went nowhere in an evolutionary sense. They are considered a divergent line of mammals. Their presence as fossils serves to highlight our lack of knowledge of the earliest mammalian development. The history of this entire group ends abruptly, without a trace of later species or a close tie to any living mammals.

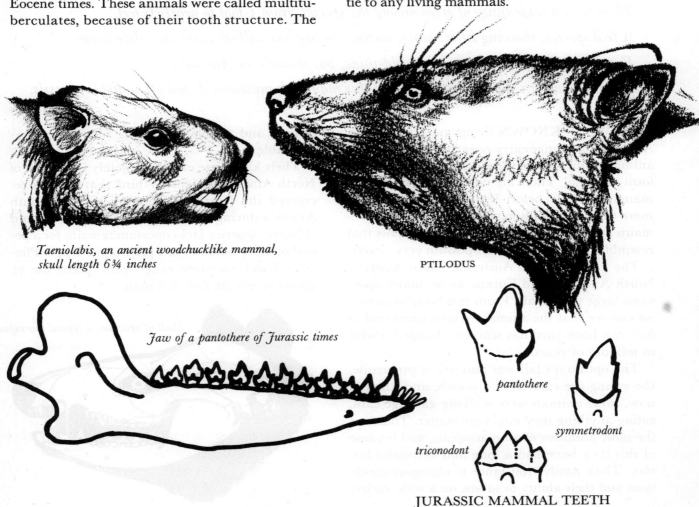

Taeniolabis, an ancient woodchucklike mammal, skull length 6¾ inches

PTILODUS

Jaw of a pantothere of Jurassic times

pantothere

symmetrodont

triconodont

JURASSIC MAMMAL TEETH

25

OPOSSUM—*a living relic*

Pronounced **o · poss · um**, *often shortened to "possum."*

The name is of American Indian origin.

There was a wide range of sizes among the species, from 1 foot to nearly 6 feet.

A few species, showing little change during the last 60 million years, are alive today.

Fossils of opossums are found world-wide, but notably in Australia.

Mounted modern species usually typify this mammal; museums do not often display fossils.

THE WELL-KNOWN living opossum of North America is a strange carry-over from the past. This animal typifies one of the oldest clear records of a fossil mammal. There are no skulls or skeletons of mammals known before Upper Cretaceous times, more than sixty million years ago. All known remains are of teeth and incomplete lower jaws that resemble those of the living opossum very closely.

The fossil record of Australia, South America, North America, and Europe shows many opossums large and small. From this bony evidence, we can see that the animal we sometimes find in our own back yard has scarcely changed a whit in millions of years.

The opossum's tail was and still is prehensile, the young are carried in a pouch, and, then as now, these animals were walking garbage cans, eating anything they might encounter. These are the most primitive of all marsupials, and because of this they have had a long and successful history. Their passive resistance to changing conditions and their ability to subsist on a wide variety of food and to live in varying habitats are remarkable.

Their kind were once completely wiped out of North America. Scientists think that the race reentered the Northern Hemisphere from South America during Pliocene times. The fossil record of North America lacks opossum remains for a period of thirty million years prior to the Upper Pliocene. Fossil opossums range from mouse size to giants nearly six feet in length.

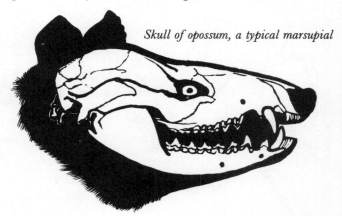

Skull of opossum, a typical marsupial

26

PHENACODUS—*one of the earliest hoofed mammals*

Pronounced **fee · nack · o · dus**

Translated, the name means "deceiver toothed," because the total body appearance is not in keeping with the tooth structure and arrangement.

The animal was about 6 feet long.

Lived during Paleocene times, 60 million years ago.

Found in Europe and western North America.

Displayed at the American Museum of Natural History in New York.

THIS IS a crude mammal typical of the entire fauna of the Paleocene. Before it was found as a fossil, authorities had formed a rather clear picture of such an animal. Many paleontologists realized that some of the older hoofed mammals must have evolved from just such a still older type.

The over-all appearance was that of a clumsy carnivorous animal, but all five toes on each foot bore blunt hoofs, and the teeth had begun to show signs of a strongly vegetable diet. The skull is rather small for such a large mammal; it resembles the numerous primitive carnivore skulls in being long and narrow with a small brain cavity.

For a long time Phenacodus was called the ancestor of the horse, but this animal is too large and well developed to be considered in this light. Its occurrence as a fossil is too late in history to permit a close relationship to the tiny Eocene four-toed horses.

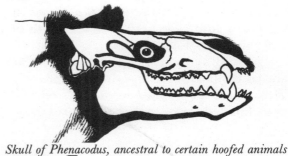

Skull of Phenacodus, ancestral to certain hoofed animals

BARYLAMBDA—*a primitive hoofed mammal*
Pronounced **bar · ee · lamb · da**

Translated, the name means "heavily sutured," referring to the skull bones.

Was approximately 8 feet long.

Lived during Paleocene and Lower Eocene times, 60 to 45 million years ago.

Found in the western United States.

Not often displayed in public museums.

THIS CRUDE-LOOKING beast was the giant of his time. Barylambda was eight feet long and stood four feet tall, a primitive hoofed mammal with a very thick long tail. The hind legs were quite long and gave the animal a rather tipped-up appearance. The blunt face and teeth suggest a grubbing, root-eating habit.

The fossil remains of this and related animals are very numerous from Lower Eocene deposits. While there are no good records of similar primitive mammals prior to that time, they must have existed, for the entire group seems to show up very suddenly and in too many different forms.

Each toe of the foot bore a well-developed hoof; the entire foot was simple and compact. The body was of narrow build. The archaic ungulates of this kind are responsible in part for scientists distinguishing part of the Lower Eocene as a separate epoch, the Paleocene. These crude mammals were so different from later forms that their importance had to be pointed up by this further division of the early Cenozoic Era.

CORYPHODON—*a crude mammal of aquatic habits*

Pronounced **ko . riff . o . don**

Translated, the name means "pointed tooth," referring to the sharp incisors.

Some species were 8 feet long; most species were about 6 feet.

Lived during Paleocene times, 60 million years ago.

Found in Wyoming and several other western states.

Displayed at the Princeton University Museum and the American Museum of Natural History, New York.

CORYPHODON was internally similar to Barylambda, but from its vertebrae anatomists deduce that it had a more rounded body. Similar large mammals with rounded bodies had nearly hairless skin and lived in a watery habitat. Coryphodon resembled a modern hippopotamus.

The teeth of this animal were rather unspecialized, but the incisors had developed into formidable, sharp-pointed tusks. Paleontologists believe that tusks of the males were much larger than those of the females.

Individual species varied considerably in size. All of these animals died out in North America in the Middle Eocene, but lived on in Asia until Lower Oligocene times, thirty-five million years ago. The fossil remains of this animal are quite numerous and typify the crude mammal fauna of Paleocene times.

Legs were short; the tail was slender and long; the heavy body was carried on five-toed feet. Coryphodon is a common fossil in this country but was first described from an English specimen.

UINTATHERIUM—*a primitive slow-footed mammal*

Pronounced **yew · in · ta · *thee* · ree · um**

Translated, the name means "the beast from the Uintas," from the mountain range in which it was first found.

The animal was about 12 feet long.

Lived during Paleocene times, between 50 and 60 million years ago.

Found only in North America, principally in the northern Uinta mountains in Utah.

Displayed in the Utah State Museum at Vernal, the Denver Natural History Museum, and in most of the large museums in the eastern United States.

THE HEAD of this strange beast is easily its most outstanding feature. The horny projections from the skull and the long fangs created a great deal of confusion when the animal was first discovered. The grotesque appearance led some to think that Uintatherium might have been related to the dinosaurs. Today we know this view to be incorrect, but we know very little more about the proper placement of the animal in the scheme of mammal evolution.

This animal is an ancient species lumped with similar archaic forms in a group called the amblypods. This word means "slow-footed" and is applied to several types of crude-hoofed mammals from Paleocene times.

The body of a Uintatherium resembled that of a small elephant. The horns on the skull of this and closely related species place them in a separate order called the Dinocerata, a word meaning "terribly horned ones."

The origin and eventual evolution of this beast are unknown. Usually only the skull parts are found; within them the brain case is small. This lack of brain must be considered an important factor in the animal's final extinction.

The head was long and narrow, the skulls of the males and females differing considerably. The lower jaw had long flanges that served to protect the tusks of the males from breakage. The largest of these animals were seven feet tall at the shoulders, and thus they were the largest animals alive during Paleocene times.

UINTATHERIUM, A SLOW-FOOTED MAMMAL

PATRIOFELIS—*a creodont*

Pronounced **pat · ree · o · feel · is**

Translated, the word means "father cat," because the creodonts were primitive flesh eaters, and in this species the skull and teeth were like those of a great cat.

Was about 9 feet long from tail tip to nose.

Lived from Paleocene to Eocene times, 60 to 45 million years ago.

Found in Wyoming and other western states.

Full skeletons are not usually displayed, but creodont skulls may be seen in all large museums.

THE WORD *creodont* means "flesh-tooth," and the animals that fall within this classification were the earliest and most primitive carnivorous mammals. Their teeth were adapted for slashing and shearing flesh.

There were many species of creodonts, and though they varied a great deal in size their general appearance must have been quite similar. The head was large, seemingly out of proportion to the body. The legs were short and stout, bearing claws that were sharp or in some species hooflike. The tail was long, and the entire body probably was covered with coarse thick hair. The skull was long and the brain case was small in all species. It is suggested that these animals behaved very much like living hyenas. Not all species were active predators; some ate carrion, and a few small types were insectivores. Whatever the species, the teeth

and jaws were strong, the dominant feature of the entire group.

Patriofelis was huge, as long as a modern lion. The skull was massive, but the legs were short and the toes widespread. The heavy tail vertebrae suggest that it was a very thick appendage. This feature plus the leg and foot structure indicate that the animal may have been partially aquatic, not unlike a huge otter.

Some creodonts lived in Asia and Africa until Pliocene times, about ten million years ago. In North America most of them died out thirty-five million years ago, in the Oligocene. The skeletons of these animals indicate that they were not habitually swift-moving. Many of them fed on the primitive hoofed mammals, and as these forms died out most carnivorous creodonts disappeared. The hyenalike scavengers survived longest.

Skull of Oxyaena, a creodont, length 8¼ inches

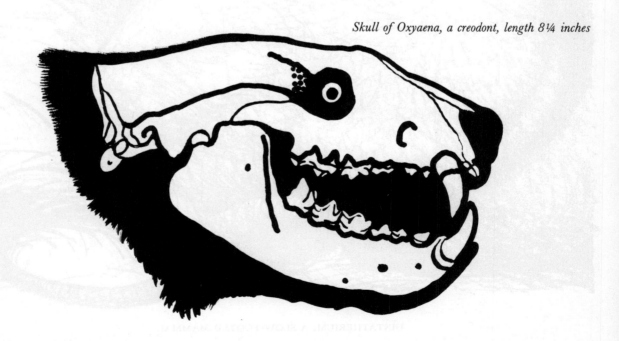

PATRIOFELIS, A CREODONT OF PALEOCENE TIMES

TITANOTHERIUM, ONE OF THE BEST-KNOWN MAMMALS FROM THE WESTERN UNITED STATES

TITANOTHERIUM—*a giant related to the horses*

Pronounced **ty · tan · o · thee · ree · um**

Translated, the name means "titanic beast."

Largest species was 8 feet high at the shoulder and well over 15 feet in total length.

Lived during Eocene and Lower Oligocene times, 50 until 35 million years ago.

Found principally in the Bad Lands of South Dakota.

Full skeletons are rather rare in museums; most institutions display a skull alone to represent the animal.

TITANOTHERIUM was one of the most numerous and spectacular mammals of the North American continent. When first discovered, its remains focused international attention on the Bad Lands of South Dakota and the possibilities of finding important new fossils there.

This is one of the earliest representatives of a large mammal group called the perissodactyls (odd-toed, hoofed mammals). Horses, rhinoceroses, chalicotheres (perissodactyls, but with claws rather than hoofs on the feet), and titanotheres are all closely related within this grouping. There is no clear explanation for the disappearance of all four animals from North America.

The remarkable rise of the titanotheres in our fossil history is exemplified by their tendency to become giants. From the numerous fossils that have been found they are well known. Their small brains and generalized body structure must have limited their eventual success during the Age of Mammals.

The male animals had broad horns above the nose; these grew longer and more widespread than those of the females. For many years these horns have been carefully measured, and many new species have been proposed on the basis of their size, but it is now agreed that in the later stages of evolution among titanotheres there was really only one major species. All of the wide variety of horns was really no different than the variation in the horns of individual modern cattle.

There is a division of opinion going on continuously in the science of paleontology, and it affects all classifications of animals. Some students diligently measure each bone and then develop mathematical formulas to help define species. These people freely refer to themselves as "hairsplitters." In contrast to this concentration on details there is the method of those who call themselves "lumpers." These men ignore minor changes in bone size and favor a general definition of a species on the basis of more obvious structural differences. Since titanotheres from the Dakota Bad Lands come from a single, rather narrow layer of rock, it seems reasonable to assume that they were all of the same species and that the "lumpers" are correct in their thinking in this instance.

None of this means that there was only one kind of titanothere, for the group as a whole came into being during Lower Eocene times and flourished strongly for fully ten million years. During such a long period several kinds of skulls developed. The earliest were small and without horns; in later forms the total proportions of the head were variable, along with a variety of horn shapes. While these skull changes were going on, the body proportions were also varying. However, the feet of these mammals remained unspecialized. The legs were short and massive to help support a very heavy skeleton and body.

Until recently, the remains of titanotheres were unknown outside of the United States. But as new finds were made in Asia and eastern Europe, the cause for the extinction of all titanotheres became clearer. It seems that their teeth were rather unspecialized and could not withstand the wear they had to undergo in chewing the tough grasses of a changing habitat.

Individual titanotheres grew tremendous nasal horns that were at one time supposed to have been a protection against predatory beasts. These same individuals were more than fifteen feet long and stood eight feet high at the shoulder. It seems unlikely that so large an animal had need to fear the rather small predators that existed in the earliest Oligocene times. The horns may have been a sexual distinction rather than a defensive asset.

35

HEADS OF TITANOTHERES

(Oldest form on the bottom)

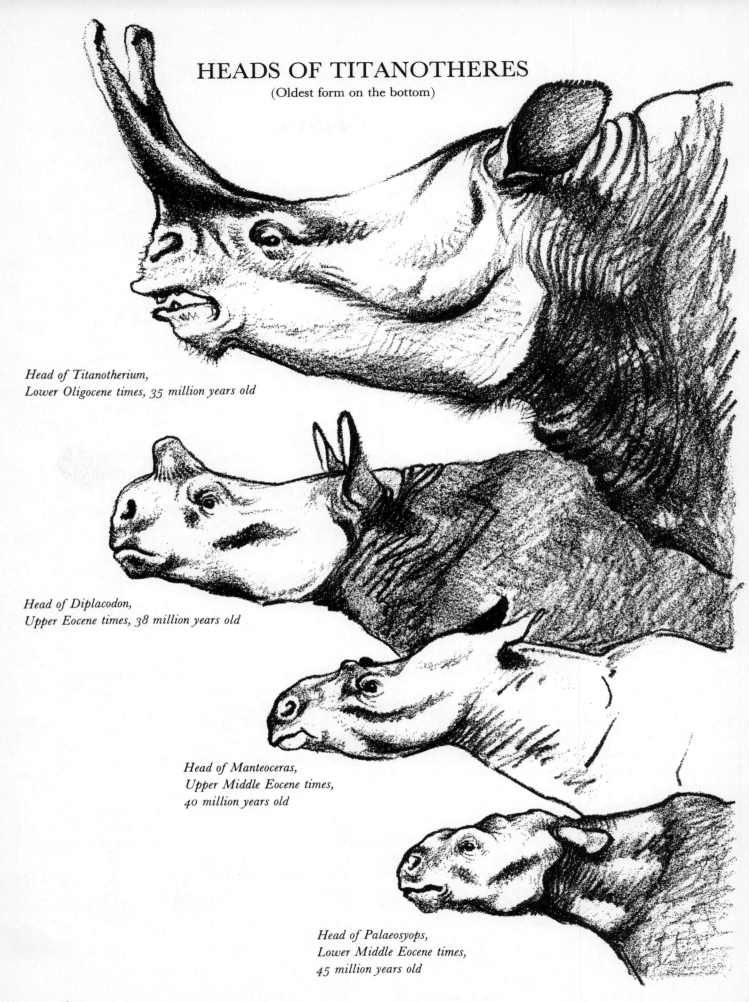

Head of Titanotherium,
Lower Oligocene times, 35 million years old

Head of Diplacodon,
Upper Eocene times, 38 million years old

Head of Manteoceras,
Upper Middle Eocene times,
40 million years old

Head of Palaeosyops,
Lower Middle Eocene times,
45 million years old

BRAIN SIZE OF THREE MAMMALS

Brain size in a primitive Eocene uintathere

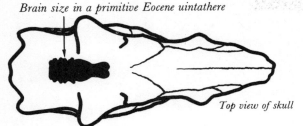

Top view of skull

Brain size in an Oligocene titanothere

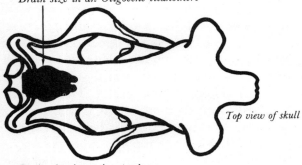

Top view of skull

Brain size in an ice age horse

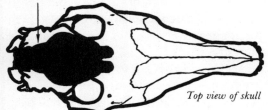

Top view of skull

FEET OF VARIOUS PERISSODACTYLS

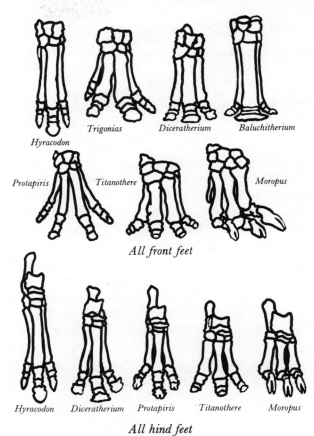

Hyracodon *Trigonias* *Diceratherium* *Baluchitherium*

Protapiris *Titanothere* *Moropus*

All front feet

Hyracodon *Diceratherium* *Protapiris* *Titanothere* *Moropus*

All hind feet

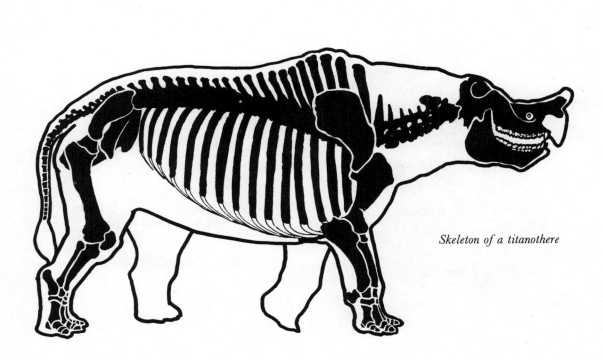

Skeleton of a titanothere

MOROPUS—*an anatomical puzzle*

Pronounced **more · o · pus**

Translated, the name means "foolish-footed."

This animal was about the size and general build of a modern horse.

Lived during Lower Miocene times, 25 million years ago.

Found in western North America.

Displayed in all of the larger natural history museums.

FOR MANY years the bones of this animal were a riddle to science, because its upper body and its feet were thought to be parts of two entirely different animals. This situation came about because the skull and body bones seemed to place the animal perfectly among the perissodactyls (odd-toed, hoofed mammals). But the feet are of unusual construction and did not bear hoofs; instead, they bore three stout claws. Eventually a fully articulated skeleton was discovered, and a final identification was made possible. The structural peculiarities of this mammal led to a separate classification for the types; they are called chalicotheres.

Judging by the teeth, it is felt that Moropus was a browser. The teeth in the front of the mouth were weak or entirely absent. Those to the rear of the jaw were stout and structurally similar to the teeth of titanotheres. The claws on the feet which had confused the picture of the animal's feeding habits must have been used to dig roots.

This digging habit is further confirmed by the stout shoulders and the areas for strong muscle attachment on the bones of the upper back.

The hind legs were shorter than the front legs. When first found, the leg and foot bones were thought to belong to an anteater. The structure of the skull suggests that a short trunk or snout might have been present. This helps to confirm the digging habits. In contrast, some authorities believe that Moropus lived in the forest and used the claws to drag down tree branches while standing on its hind legs. Such a posture could also help explain the longer front legs and the possibility of the existence of a trunk.

The species within this group that are found in North America are most distinctive, but there were many older forms about the size of sheep. There were also later species, now entirely disappeared from earth, in Asia and Africa. These animals were a side line of perissodactyl evolution. They left no living descendants.

Skull of Moropus, 24 inches long

MOROPUS, A HORSELIKE COMPOSITE OF PECULIAR ANATOMICAL FEATURES

TUPAIA—*a modern tree shrew*

Pronounced **too · *py* · ah**

Translated, the name, from Malay, means "squirrel," a reference to its tree-dwelling habits.

The animal is about 18 inches in total length.

Lives in the Orient today. Its ancestry goes back 35 million years into Oligocene times.

Mounted specimens of the living form are displayed in the largest museums.

Fossil shrews are seldom displayed anywhere.

THIS living mammal typifies a large number of fossil forms. They are considered to have been close to the basic stock from which all placental mammals arose. The trend toward an advanced stage of development at birth began, far back in Eocene times, among mammals like these.

The shrewlike animals were abundant and assumed many forms. They rapidly replaced the numerous marsupials and other crude mammals. By contrast to the older types, they were more active and had correspondingly larger brains.

This animal and its close relatives were primarily insectivores, carnivorous mammals which prefer a diet of insects but also eat other food, and in many ways their bodies show structural patterns that are repeated in the earliest primate skeletons. Most species have been small, with large eyes and short legs, and they might well have been active at night in a treetop habitat. Their teeth have stayed close to a fixed dental formula.

Such small animals represent one of the last, almost untouched areas of fossil study. The evidence their often fragmentary remains offers may some day fill out many of the unsolved puzzles of mammalian evolution; the possible link between insectivores and primates is particularly fascinating.

The star-nosed mole, typical modern insectivorous animal

40

NOTHARCTUS—*a primitive form of lemur*

Pronounced **no · thark · tus**

Translated, the name means "false bear," because it was first thought to be a bear.
Was 3 feet long, including the tail.
Lived during Eocene times, 50 million years ago.
Found in Wyoming.
Finest specimens are shown at the American Museum of Natural History in New York.

THIS IS a very significant fossil animal. It is the only representative of the ape family in this book. It serves to illustrate that the monkeys and apes were a prominent feature in the North American faunal lists very early in mammalian history.

The skull and skeletal parts of Notharctus have been vigorously debated in an effort to place it with several animal families. This happens because the remains show anatomical features that are common to several seemingly unrelated animal groups.

The skulls illustrated here show clearly the tremendous change that spans fifty million years, from Eocene times until the near-human skull of Australopithecus of the late ice age in South Africa.

Notharctus, when discovered, created a great stir in science, for it had previously been supposed that the primates were of much more recent origin. The bones of this and similar specimens are fifty million years old, but they must have an ancestry that is considerably older.

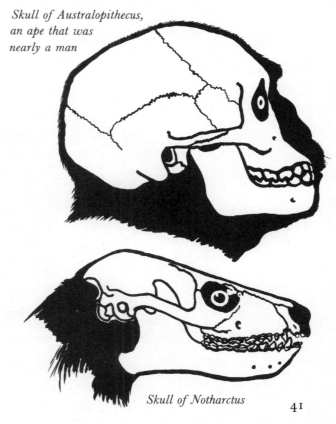

Skull of Australopithecus, an ape that was nearly a man

Skull of Notharctus

41

ARSINOITHERIUM—*a giant from Egypt*

Pronounced ar . *sin* . o . e . thee . ree . um

Translated, the name means "beast of Arsinoe," because the remains were first found near that Egyptian city.

This animal was 11 feet long, 5½ feet high at the shoulders.

Lived during Lower Oligocene times, 35 million years ago.

Found in Egypt and other parts of northern Africa.

The skeleton is not displayed in this country.

THESE peculiar mammals are placed in a separate order that seems to strike a medium between the elephant and the tiny hyrax. Arsinoitheres flourished strongly at a time when the rhinoceroses were just beginning to evolve and spread over much of the world. These animals occupied the same ecological place in the African fauna that later rhinoceros forms occupied all over the world.

As with so many "old-fashioned" mammals, the body of this beast does not show a great deal of specialization. The significant feature is the head. On it four horns were distinctive. Those of the males were long and sharp. The horns of the female and the young were less conspicuous and were rounded. The tremendous size of the front pair of horns seems to have required extra support, which was provided in the form of a bar of bone that projected from the base of the horns between the nostrils and was attached to the upper jawbone.

The feet of this animal were large, and the five toes were widespread. The legs were short and the neck was short. The structure of the teeth would indicate that these animals were exclusively grazers.

Virtually nothing is known of the ancestry or the descendants of this animal. It is only in the tooth structure that science has any clue to preceding forms. The teeth of the hyrax and those of this Oligocene giant are in many ways similar. The elephantine body of Arsinoitherium seems to offer further evidence that this animal is in some way a part of the story of elephant evolution.

THE HYRAX

ARSINOITHERIUM, RELATED TO ELEPHANTS AND SEA COWS

MOERITHERIUM—*ancestor of the elephants*

Pronounced **mee · ree · thee · ree · um**

Translated, the name means "beast from Lake Moeris," because it was found near this lake.

Stood just over 3 feet high at the shoulder, about the bulk of a modern tapir.

Lived between Upper Eocene and Lower Oligocene times, 40 million years ago.

Found at Lake Moeris in northern Egypt.

Skeletons are not displayed in this country. Often shown as a scale model or in a full restoration of the head alone.

IN SEVERAL instances where fossil-hunters have a long series of animal remains to work with, the inevitable question arises, "Where did these animals originate?" With fossil elephants this situation did exist. The bones of large recent animals of this group are known from every continent but Australia. Though the fossil record shows some gradual change in size and an increased specialization for feeding, no clear ancestor to the entire group was known for many years.

By returning to the continent where living elephants are numerous and where their fossil remains are also abundant, excavators presumed that they might find the missing ancestral animal. This very thing happened in Egypt. The skeleton and skull of Moeritherium were unearthed from the Faiyum deposits in the northern part of that country. The layered earth that held the bones dates from Eocene deposits forty-five million years old.

From the skeletal structure it is safe to assume that this ancestral form probably behaved very much like a modern hippopotamus, never straying too far from the river bottom lands.

Moeritherium was small, only about three feet high at the shoulders. This animal had a rather large head, and its incisor teeth were quite long, an indication of the tusks that were to develop in later forms. From the position of the nostrils in the skull it is evident that there was no lengthening of the snout into a trunk, but the placement of the nostrils had already shifted slightly from the front to the upper portions of the skull.

It is fitting that this ancient beast was found on the continent of Africa, the home of the impressive elephant that is the largest land mammal alive today. Asiatic elephants alive today do not equal the African species in height or tusk size, though rare individuals might weigh nearly as much.

44

PALEOMASTODON—*a primitive elephant form*

Pronounced **pay . lee . o .** *mas* **. to . don**

Translated, the name means "ancient nipple tooth."

Was about 6 feet high at the shoulders.

Known from Lower Oligocene times, 35 million years ago.

Found in the Faiyum, southwest of Cairo, Egypt.

Original material is not displayed in this country.

AFTER the discovery of Moeritherium, two other early elephantlike forms were also found in Egypt. Both differed from the ancestral form, not only in size, but in that they had also developed prominent tusks in the upper and lower jaws. Both animals come from Oligocene deposits that date thirty-five million years into the past.

During the ten-million-year span of one of these animals, Phiomia, it attained a height of four feet at the shoulder and developed a short trunk. Its teeth had become somewhat complicated and give indication of a change in diet that was related to the use of the lower tusks for digging roots and other tough material.

Paleomastodon is the form illustrated in this drawing and it stood six feet tall at the shoulder. Most scientists regard this animal as an offshoot from the main line of elephants that developed in succeeding epochs. The nostrils and upper lip were not quite a trunk, and the teeth had begun to develop prominent, simple cusps for cutting coarse foodstuff. All of the body features were progressive ones, and the skull and teeth of elephants that were to follow became more specialized and refined in detail.

Both animals undoubtedly stayed close to watery places in jungle country. In spite of this tropical habitat, the skin was probably quite hair-covered and thick.

45

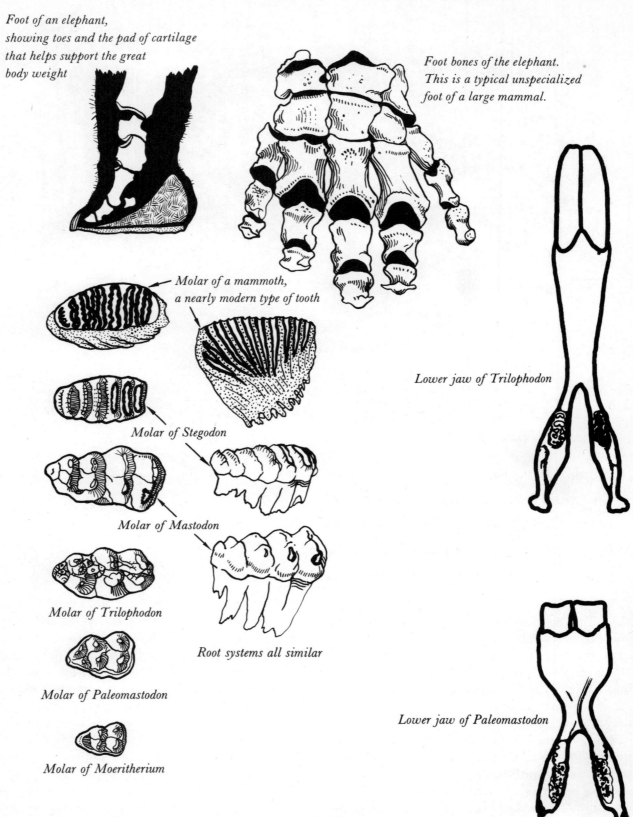

Foot of an elephant, showing toes and the pad of cartilage that helps support the great body weight

Foot bones of the elephant. This is a typical unspecialized foot of a large mammal.

Molar of a mammoth, a nearly modern type of tooth

Molar of Stegodon

Molar of Mastodon

Root systems all similar

Molar of Trilophodon

Molar of Paleomastodon

Molar of Moeritherium

Lower jaw of Trilophodon

Lower jaw of Paleomastodon

Evolution of various elephant teeth toward an efficient
grass-grinding surface of the modern types

TYPICAL SKULL STRUCTURE IN VARIOUS ELEPHANT SPECIES

Skull of a typical mammoth

Skull of a typical mastodon

Skull of a primitive elephant, Paleomastodon

Skull of a typical long-jawed elephant, Trilophodon

Skull of the ancestral elephant, Moeritherium

TRILOPHODON—*a long-jawed elephant*

Pronounced try . lof . o . don

Translated, the name means "three-crested tooth."

Was about 10 feet long.

Various species lived over a period of 20 million years from Lower Miocene until Upper Pliocene times.

Found in Texas and in other isolated areas of central western states.

Usually only the skull is displayed, and even that is often a cast from the rather scarce original bone.

IN THE long history of elephants and their relatives, there were steady increases in size leading up into modern times.

During the Miocene Epoch, there was apparently a migration of elephant types into North America, and among the migrating species was one group of animals different because of its long lower jaw.

In Trilophodon, the lower tusks of many specimens show a great deal of wear due to digging. The upper tusks grew out to a length equal to those of the lower jaw. Apparently these specialized upper teeth were not used in any way except possibly as a defense measure.

Some of these long-jawed elephants dominated the paleontological history of the Miocene for ten to fifteen million years. In at least one species the maximum length of the lower jaw reached an incredible seven feet.

There was a trunk, but it did not extend much beyond the end of the lower tusks. The individual teeth of some species had numerous cusps, an indication of a continuing diet of coarse food.

In the succeeding millions of years that led into Pliocene times, the long lower jaw began to shorten and the trunk to lengthen. This type of elephant died out on the African continent without leaving any direct descendants.

It is supposed from its jaw and tooth structure that this was a forest-dwelling elephant. Its remains are quite numerous in many parts of the world.

TRILOPHODON, A LONG-JAWED ANIMAL FOUND IN TEXAS

DINOTHERIUM—*a peculiar-looking elephant*

Pronounced **dy · no · *thee* · ree · um**

Translated, the name means "terrible beast."

Was about 12 feet high at the shoulders, one of the larger elephant species.

This type of elephant persisted from Early Miocene until Late Pleistocene times, 25 million years.

Found in Africa and Asia; not known from North American deposits.

Not displayed in this country.

IN ANY large and varied group of animals, there are often several distinct lines evolving during any given historical period. In the case of the elephants, there were at least three separate evolutionary trends thriving from Miocene times until the end of the Pliocene Epoch. These three groups were, first, the numerous long-jawed species; second, the many typical elephants evolving toward the living species of today, and, in Europe and Asia, a strange third line called dinotheres. Their bones are found over a wide geographic area.

The evolutionary growth of the dinotheres was slow and steady. The line survived in Africa until the ice age, and by that time the individuals had grown in size to equal the largest known elephants and mastodons. The dinothere had a long trunk, and in every feature but its teeth and tusks was exactly like other elephants.

Dinotherium was unusual because there were no tusks in the upper jaw; however, there were huge ones in the lower jaw. These grew downward, and the tips curved backward for no apparent reason. The remaining teeth were rather primitive, showing primarily grinding surfaces. Not too many specimens of Dinotherium are known. It appears that this animal did not reach North America in its migrations.

The individual species increased in size as time passed, but research finds no structural link to the true elephants in this animal. The dinotheres are considered an offshoot from the main line of elephant progress.

DINOTHERIUM, A SPECIES OF ELEPHANT NOT FOUND IN THIS COUNTRY

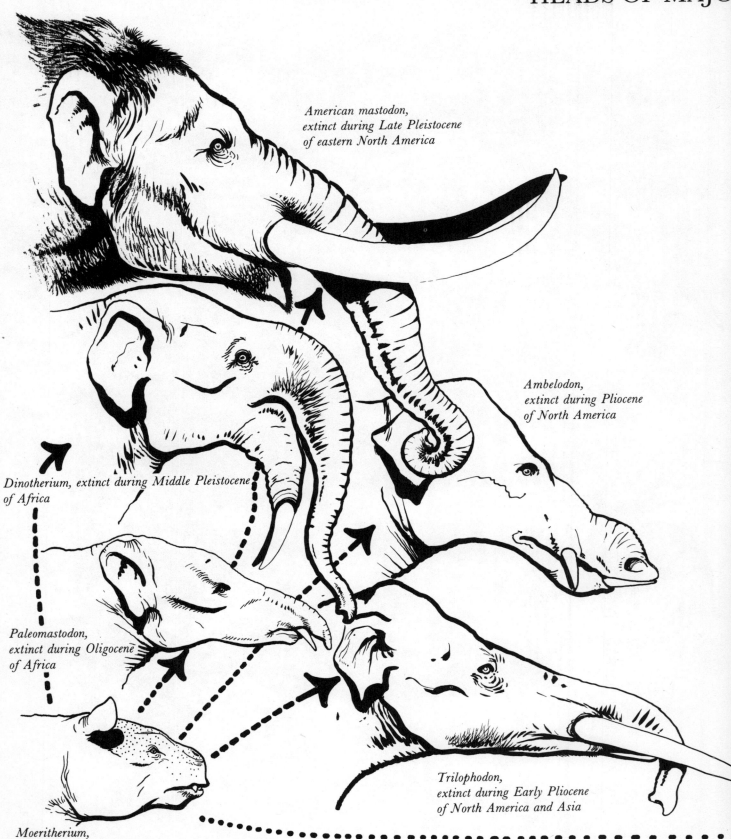

American mastodon,
extinct during Late Pleistocene
of eastern North America

Ambelodon,
extinct during Pliocene
of North America

Dinotherium, extinct during Middle Pleistocene
of Africa

Paleomastodon,
extinct during Oligocene
of Africa

Trilophodon,
extinct during Early Pliocene
of North America and Asia

Moeritherium,
ancestral to elephants, extinct during Middle Eocene of Africa

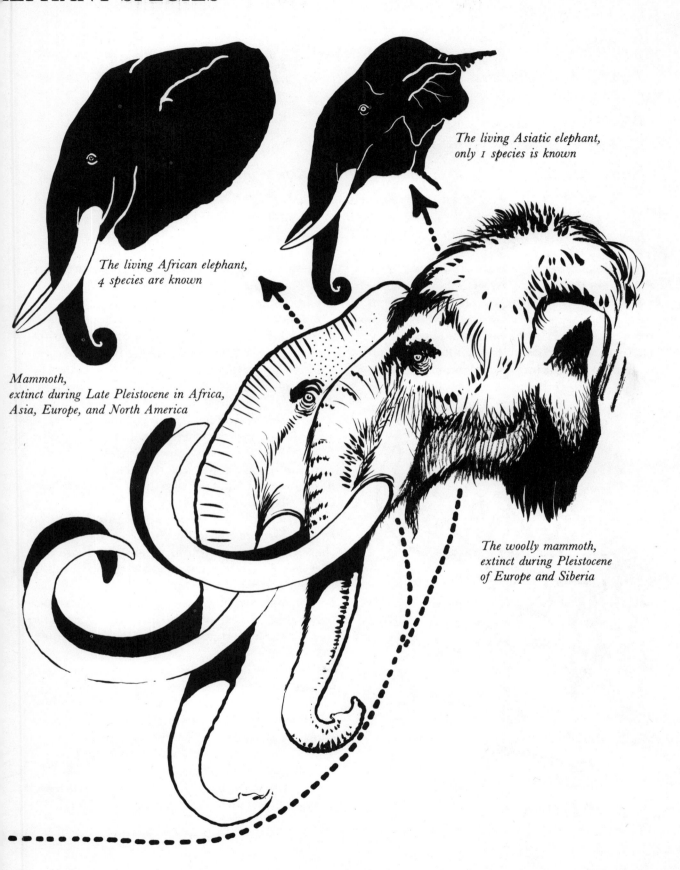

The living Asiatic elephant, only 1 species is known

The living African elephant, 4 species are known

Mammoth,
extinct during Late Pleistocene in Africa, Asia, Europe, and North America

The woolly mammoth, extinct during Pleistocene of Europe and Siberia

AMERICAN MASTODON—a dweller in the spruce forests

Pronounced **mas · to · don**

Translated, the name means "nipple tooth," because of the conical shape of the cusps on each tooth.

Was about 9 feet 6 inches high at the shoulders.

Lived in North America after the last glaciation, 15,000 to possibly 8,000 years ago.

Found principally in the eastern United States adjacent to the Great Lakes.

Finest specimens are displayed in the Cleveland Museum of Natural History and the American Museum of Natural History in New York City. Many museums display parts of skeletons or composite animals.

IN MANY of the eastern United States there are frequent finds of mastodon bones. This animal was a forest dweller that fed on the coarse twigs from the evergreen forest that covered North America following the retreat of the last great glaciers.

There is controversy over whether men and mastodons ever came into direct contact. Scattered evidence would indicate that they did, for it is difficult to believe that any animal so numerous, that lived so late in our history, could have escaped some contact with early man.

Climate, however, may have had something to do with keeping such meetings infrequent, for the early hunters may have been held in check by the cold of the north country. The boggy terrain favored by these animals may also have been too dangerous or too full of insects for man's liking.

Any forest-dwelling animal is apt to be rare as a fossil, because its skeleton decays quickly after death. However, mastodon remains are so numerous that some people feel they might have outnumbered the buffalo that later populated the Great Plains.

Practically every museum can cite numerous local records of mastodon finds, a great many of these from boggy ground where the dense clay and acid bog-water have helped preserve nearly complete skeletons in almost perfect condition. Some bones have tendon masses still attached when they are excavated; these tissues are often quite pliable and fresh in appearance and texture.

The deep crevices between the cusps of this animal's teeth are frequently found filled with wadded remains from its last meal. Examination of this evidence indicates that spruce and hemlock seem to have been staple items of their diet.

Mastodons were very hairy; they had round, barrellike bodies and long sloping foreheads. The tusks of the males were often ten feet in length and as much as ten inches in diameter.

Skeleton of the American mastodon

THE AMERICAN MASTODON, A COMMON INHABITANT OF NORTH AMERICA

WOOLLY MAMMOTH—*an elephant of the north country*

Pronounced **mam** · uth

The name refers to the heavy coat of long hair and great height of this animal. Scientific name: Elephas primigenius.

Stood 12 *feet high at the shoulder. One species was* 14 *feet at the shoulder.*

Lived during Pleistocene times, 1 *million until* 10,000 *years ago.*

These fossils are known from nearly every part of the Northern Hemisphere. Entire bodies have been found frozen in Siberia and Alaska.

The best fossil elephant display in this country is the Hall of Elephants at the University of Nebraska Museum in Lincoln.

AT THE end of the Pliocene and during the early Pleistocene, many different kinds of mammoth appeared in Europe, Asia, Africa, and North America. These are the forms most directly related to the living elephant of today. They were tall thin-bodied giants with short high heads and tremendous curving tusks. One North American species stood a full fourteen feet at the shoulders, and its skeleton makes one of the most spectacular vertebrate displays exhibited anywhere in this country.

Great numbers of mammoth skeletons have come from the open lands of the United States, particularly the grasslands of Florida and Kentucky. They are most numerous in Nebraska. This kind of elephant was the open country counterpart of the forest-dwelling mastodon. Its teeth bore a long, ridged, grinding surface to help it consume the grasslike plants. It did not feed on coarse material such as twigs.

The woolly mammoth with its long sweeping coat of hair was a prime subject for the primitive cave painters of Europe's Stone Age. Frozen earth of the north country has yielded complete bodies of this animal to confirm the accuracy of these drawings.

Fossil mammoth ivory has been the main source of the world's carving ivory for many years. The rivers of the Russian north have washed out thousands of paired tusks every year for export. The thawing of frozen grounds yields the bones and tusks; during flood conditions these are carried downstream and the natives collect the tusks for marketing. In New York the frozen remains of a baby mammoth are on display at the American Museum of Natural History. Frozen mammoth flesh has been sampled during at least one famous banquet, and in Alaska placer-mining operations have exposed a great deal of frozen flesh that is quickly consumed by the husky dogs. So far, there have been no harmful effects to anyone, so well preserved has the flesh been by the permafrost.

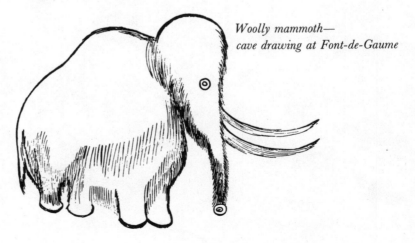

Woolly mammoth— cave drawing at Font-de-Gaume

THE WOOLLY MAMMOTH, OFTEN FOUND FROZEN IN ARCTIC COUNTRIES

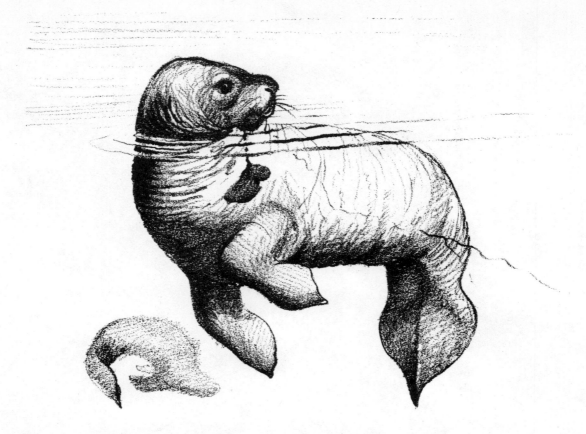

MANATEE and DUGONG—*related to the elephant*

Members of the order Sirenia *(pronounced* **si · reen · ya** *): the name refers to the notion that the near-human faces of these animals were responsible for the legends of sirens or mermaids.*

Average length, 9 feet.

Fossils known from Eocene times, 50 million years ago, until the present. Several species are alive today; the Florida manatee is the only one in this country.

Fossils are not generally displayed.

Manatees and DUGONGS—the sea cows —have evolved a long way from elephant forms, but they are structurally related to these giants of the land.

Many people claim that myths of mermaids and mermen find their origin in this aquatic mammal. Because they are mammals, the females nurse their young; in doing so, they rear their bodies part way out of the water. By using some imagination, the rounded head, the face, and the upper body of this animal could be said to resemble that of a human being. The heavy whiskers some individuals bear might also suggest the face of an old man.

These water dwellers inhabit rivers; living species are shy and seldom appear on the water's surface in broad daylight. When they are seen at all, the lighting is often bad and the atmosphere likely to be misty. Under poor observing conditions, the myth of the mermaid could have been created.

The skeleton of this animal shows no trace of hind legs. The teeth are simple and adapted to eating soft vegetation. The nostrils are high on the head, and the breathing apparatus is much modified to permit long periods under water with a slow rate of oxygen consumption.

Primitive forms are known from the West Indies and Africa. These animals were already near their present-day form when the elephants were still in their earliest stages of evolution. The group as a whole became distinctive fifty million years ago. Most good fossils of these animals are known from northern Africa and southeast Asia.

58

EOHIPPUS—*a tiny four-toed horse*

Pronounced **ee · o · hip · us**

Translated, the name means "dawn horse."

Was about 12 to 14 inches high at the shoulder.

Lived about 50 million years ago.

Finest skeletons have come from Colorado.

Restored skeletons or replicas of at least the skull and foot are displayed in all large U. S. museums.

ONE OF the outstanding series of fossils displayed anywhere is the dramatic collection of horse types in the American Museum of Natural History. A steady and progressive evolution is illustrated in a sequence of skulls and feet that offers one of the clearest arguments for the entire theory of evolution.

The first and smallest horse in this series is Eohippus, the dawn horse. His body was hardly bigger than that of a rabbit; his front legs bore four toes on the feet, and the hind feet had three toes each. The entire skeleton was poorly known until several years ago, when an impressive deposit of these animals was unearthed at Gardner, Colorado. Closely related forms are the slightly larger Orohippus and Epihippus.

These horses were quick-moving little animals that lived in grassy open places. The untold generations of horses that followed them spread over the earth as the grasslands spread. Feeding in the open and vulnerable to attack from the numerous predators of their times, horses developed strong running legs and a reduction of the toes to a single hoof that permitted more efficient movement on hard level ground. Tooth structures in all horses vary in detail but are alike in becoming more molarized to allow feeding on tough grass.

Oligocene horses in North America were predominantly three-toed species typified by Mesohippus, an animal the size of a large dog.

In earliest Miocene times most horses still had three toes, but only the enlarged central toe was in direct contact with the ground at all times. Also in earliest Miocene times two species of horses showed an evolutionary tendency to become smaller rather than to continue the steady rate of growth that typifies the horse ancestry.

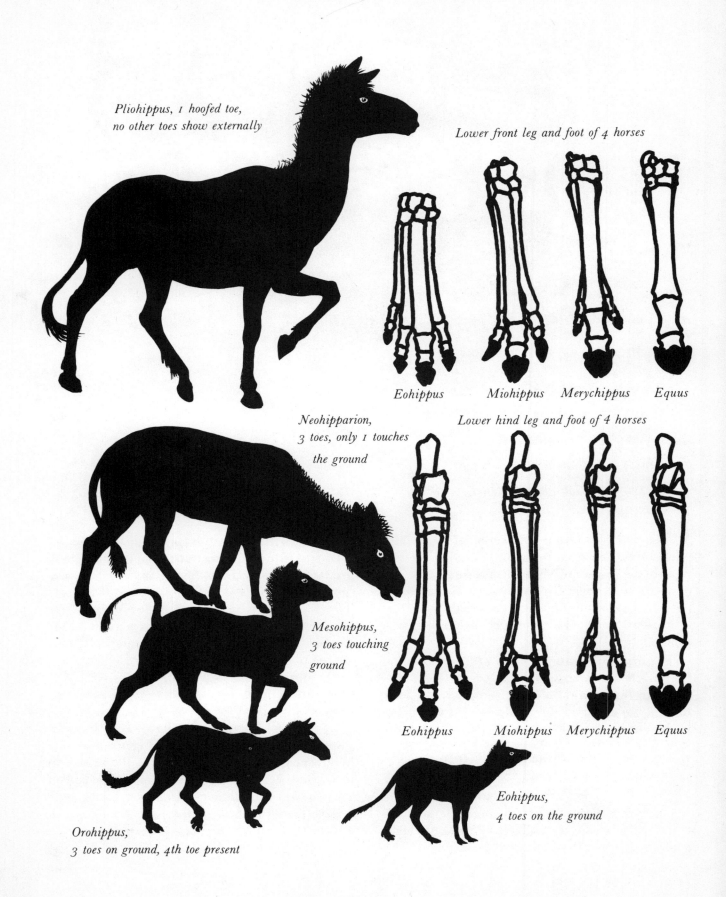

Pliohippus, 1 hoofed toe,
no other toes show externally

Lower front leg and foot of 4 horses

Eohippus   Miohippus   Merychippus   Equus

Neohipparion,
3 toes, only 1 touches
the ground

Lower hind leg and foot of 4 horses

Mesohippus,
3 toes touching
ground

Eohippus   Miohippus   Merychippus   Equus

Orohippus,
3 toes on ground, 4th toe present

Eohippus,
4 toes on the ground

60

OF THE HORSE

Modern horse, smaller than most ice age horses that inhabited North America.
Single hoofed toe. In some modern Arabian horses there are no splint bones
in the leg; this marks the complete change from 4 toes to a single hoofed toe.

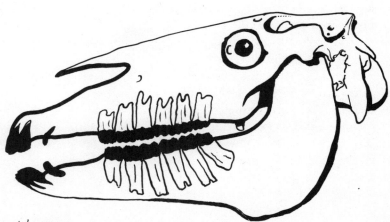

Skull of a young modern horse.
The tooth pattern is typical of all recent horses
and most difficult to distinguish from late ice age species.

EQUUS—*the ice age horse*

Pronounced **ee · kwus**

Equus is the Latin word for "horse."

At least one species was slightly taller and several species had larger heads than the modern horse.

Fossils are known from many parts of the world; they are particularly numerous in the Plains States of the United States.

This type of horse is usually represented in nearly every large U. S. natural history museum. It need not be represented by a full skeleton.

THE GENUS of horses called *Equus* typifies the ice age along with mammoths, mastodons, and similar large mammals. This horse was completely modern and nearly world-wide in distribution; our own horses are members of the same genus. In our own country someone is continually finding bones of extinct horses and refusing to believe that the strange large teeth and spectacular spines on the vertebrae of the shoulder region could possibly belong to any horse, let alone a fossil type.

History books have done a complete job of convincing people that there were no horses here when America was discovered, which is true. This leads nearly everyone to doubt that any modern-looking horses ever lived in the area now the United States. But this last idea does not follow from the first: horses were native to this country, they probably even originated here, but they died out completely some time after the end of the most recent ice age and it was not until they were re-introduced from Europe that horses again trod the soil on which most of their long evolution had occurred.

It takes an expert to decide whether or not horse bones of recent vintage belong to a long-forgotten farm animal or to a horse that died ten thousand years ago. The pattern of tooth structure and a few minor skeletal details are all that distinguish between these animals. It is not at all safe to rely on the burial locality to give a clear clue to the age of the specimen.

The animal in this drawing had a large head, relatively short legs, and a color pattern similar to that of a living zebra. The drawing represents a European form and is intended to indicate that zebras, horses, asses, and their relatives are in reality very similar. The external appearance of zebras and horses would show them to be different in-

stantly; internally, their skeletons would give no such immediate clue to which was which, except to place them both within the horse family.

Skull of an ice age horse, 23 inches long

The fossil remains of horses are widespread throughout Europe and Asia, but the greatest abundance of known specimens comes from North American deposits. Only one type is known from South America, and it comes from Pliocene deposits.

It is supposed that horses originated in North America during Paleocene times and that their ancestors were tiny five-toed mammals with strong hind legs and hopping gait, not unlike a rabbit's.

In any group of animals where the skeletal remains are so numerous, a main thread of evolution can be detected along with many side issues of development that never amounted to much. Fossil horses show a clear main line of growth and change, from four-toed Eohippus, through fifty million years of history, to Equus, the single-toed modern horse.

EQUUS, A LARGE-HEADED POST-GLACIAL SPECIES

Horse evolution has been studied so closely that some paleontologists have compiled elaborate formulas that attempt to predict the rate of evolution in several body parts, notably the length of the skull and the bones of the lower leg. Man's efforts to produce a variety of horse breeds and perfection in a running animal have made the work of the paleontologists easier in a sense, because they have speeded up the horse's evolution. This speed-up brings change, but a corresponding decrease in man's use of horses has brought the normal pace of evolution near to a standstill.

After the retreat of the last glaciers, horses faded from the earth in every place but central Asia. They were reintroduced on the plains country of every continent about five thousand years after this widespread disappearance. Horses have sur-vived on these same plains and have persisted strongly ever since.

The horse of the ice age assumed many forms and, in a few cases, was as large as or larger than a modern horse. Certain European fossils suggest a relationship to zebras, but for the most part the wild horses of the world were shaggy, solid-colored animals. Three references help clarify our knowledge of ice age horses. One reference is the living wild asses of the Gobi Desert; another is the rare Przewalski's Horse of the Asiatic steppes; and the third is the cave paintings found in many European localities. All of these tend to agree that the basic stock of all horses was a sturdy animal with a yellowish brown coat tinged with brownish black. The tail, the mane, and the hair above the hoofs were probably black.

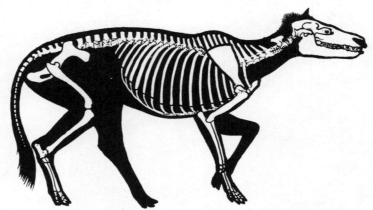

Skeleton of Eohippus

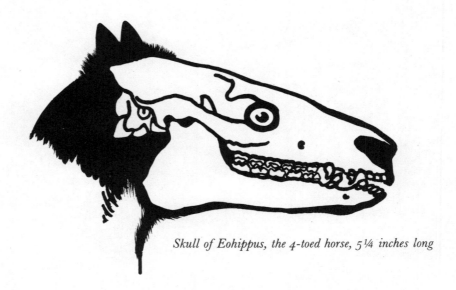

Skull of Eohippus, the 4-toed horse, 5¼ inches long

HYRACODON—*a small hornless rhinoceros*

Pronounced **hy · rack · o · don**

Translated, the word means "shrew-mouse toothed," because of individual tooth structure.

Was 5 feet long.

Lived during Oligocene times, 35 million years ago.

Found in the South Dakota Bad Lands and similar localities in the western United States.

Displayed at the Princeton Museum, University of Kansas Museum, University of Nebraska Museum, and in many other museums throughout this country.

THE RHINOCEROSES were a numerous group of mammals in practically all epochs from the Oligocene to the present. Here in North America there were many species. These are divided into five large family groups:

1. Running rhinoceroses, typified by Hyracodon.
2. The amynodonts, typified by the aquatic species Metamynodon.
3. The early true rhinoceroses, typified by hornless Caenopus.
4. The giant rhinoceroses, typified by Baluchitherium.
5. Fully modern rhinoceroses, typified by Teloceros and the woolly rhinoceros.

Hyracodon typifies the first of these groups. All of its members were good runners and, because of this fact, they are called cursorial rhinoceroses. It was a horselike small animal whose light build was well adapted to a swift-moving, open-country life.

The head of this animal was rather large for its small body. Its molar teeth were completely rhinoceroslike even at this early date in the family's development.

There was a smaller near-relative, called Hyrachyus, that had four toes and is considered by some to be a possible ancestor of the horses as well as the rhinoceroses.

All of these running types resemble horses a little more than they do rhinoceroses. Some were no larger than a hound, while other species were nearly as large as a full-grown horse.

The bones of Hyracodon are rather well represented in all museums. They abound in the Bad Lands of the Dakotas and are a typical animal in the Oligocene fauna. Their most significant body adaptations are in their feet and molar teeth.

BALUCHITHERIUM—*the largest land mammal yet discovered*

Pronounced **ba · *luke* · e · thee · ree · um**

Translated, the name means "beast from Baluchistan."

This animal was slightly more than 18 feet tall at the shoulders. Its bulk was tremendous.

Lived during Miocene times, 20 million years ago.

Found in Baluchistan in Asia.

The only specimen is owned by the American Museum of Natural History in New York.

THE DISCOVERY of this beast was part of the most wonderful fossil-hunting expedition ever organized, the Roy Chapman Andrews expedition of 1921 to 1924 to central Asia and the Gobi Desert. It was on this same trip that many new dinosaurs were discovered and the first dinosaur eggs found.

Rhinoceroses were very numerous for fifty million years, but this creature is the most unusual species of them all. The head of Baluchitherium was four and a half feet long. Even at that length, it was small in proportion to the animal's tremendous body. Though this animal was eighteen feet tall, its neck was quite long, and this feature, plus the size of the head, made it capable of reaching twenty-five feet above the ground for leaves and twigs.

The entire appearance of this animal was narrow. The bones of the legs were abnormally long.

The toes were stubby and seem scarcely broad enough to support the towering body.

Baluchitherium had only two front teeth, a pair of incisors. There was a thick pad of cartilage in the front of the jaw which served as a platform against which food was crushed. The grinding teeth were well formed for aid in consuming coarse twigs.

The rhinoceros and the horse seem to expand and develop in a parallel fashion from Eocene times until the present. The rhinos were more conservative and bulky; they disappeared to a great extent in Miocene times. Horses flourished in later Pleistocene times. Neither kind of animal has held his own during the Age of Man. Horses, because of their usefulness to man, can expect to continue living well. The rhinoceros is a tough, short-tempered beast that has become an oddity of the zoo and game preserve.

Skull of Baluchitherium, length 4 feet 6 inches

Skull of a Pliocene rhinoceros, 24 inches long

BALUCHITHERIUM, ONE OF THE WONDERS OF MAMMALIAN LIFE

TELOCEROS—*a short-legged rhinoceros*

Pronounced **tell · o · sair · us**

Translated, the name means "end horn," because the horn is on the end of the nose.

This animal was about 11 feet long.

Lived during Miocene times, 24 million years ago.

Skeletons are found in the Plains States of western North America and in scattered localities in many other places in the world.

Fine specimens are displayed in the Denver Museum; the University Museum at Lincoln, Nebraska; the Carnegie Museum, Pittsburgh; the University Museum at Princeton, New Jersey, and many other places.

RHINOCEROSES ancestral to Teloceros migrated into North America during Miocene times. These were vigorous animals. To judge by their fossil remains, they established themselves rapidly and soon replaced earlier forms or drove them into new territories.

This type of rhinoceros is essentially modern. It was probably the kind of stock from which at least four other more modern rhinoceroses originated. These include the living African and Asiatic species as well as certain ice age types. Though the end of the skull bears a roughened hump that served to anchor the horn, the horn itself was not very conspicuous and in most individuals must have been little more than a knob projecting through the skin.

It was stated in the preceding pages that the older rhinoceros families were divided into five groups. The fifth, the modern rhinoceros group, which includes Teloceros, is further subdivided into five distinct groups, some of them alive today in tropical countries:

1. Short-legged species, typified by Teloceros.
2. The true rhinoceroses, typified by the Javanese and Indian single-horned species.
3. The single-horned rhinoceroses of the ice age that were without incisors.
4. The two-horned rhinoceros, typified by the Sumatran species retaining incisors.
5. The two-horned rhinoceros, typified by the African "white" and "black" species that are without incisors.

VARIOUS RHINOCEROS HEADS (Not drawn to scale)

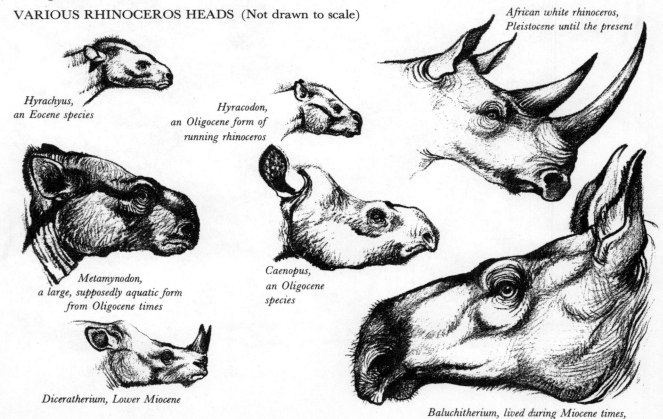

Hyrachyus, an Eocene species

Hyracodon, an Oligocene form of running rhinoceros

African white rhinoceros, Pleistocene until the present

Metamynodon, a large, supposedly aquatic form from Oligocene times

Caenopus, an Oligocene species

Diceratherium, Lower Miocene

Baluchitherium, lived during Miocene times, the largest land mammal on record

TELOCEROS, A LARGE, RATHER COMMON MIOCENE MAMMAL

WOOLLY RHINOCEROS—*a mammal of the European plains*

Pronounced **ry · nos · er · us**

Translated, the word means "nose horn."

Was 14 to 16 feet long.

Known from Late Pliocene through Pleistocene times, a span of approximately 6 million years.

Found in European caves and river deposits over a vast area.

A mounted specimen is displayed in the National Museum at Cracow, Poland.

THIS RHINOCEROS was a dominant animal of the ice age in Europe. In structure and over-all appearance it did not differ much from species living in Africa today; it was a modern animal.

A coat of long heavy hair was one factor that enabled this animal to live in the open snowy meadows of northern Europe. In Poland, completely preserved woolly rhinoceroses have been excavated. The Polish discoveries were made in soil saturated with crude oil. This material helped to preserve the flesh, bones, hair, and hide. In one instance, the body was mounted and placed on display. The hairy outer covering was evident at the time of excavation, but it was not possible to preserve it in the mounting.

This kind of rhinoceros is frequently represented in the cave drawings of primitive man. Parts of the animal's skeleton are often found within these same cave dwellings and in close relationship to the campfires of Cro-Magnon men.

This species is related to the white rhinoceros of Africa. Its hairy coat was not uniformly thick but seems to have been heavier over the shoulders and upper neck.

Cave art from Font-de-Gaume
Woolly rhinoceros

Bushman drawing, Cape Province, Africa—Rhinoceros

THE WOOLLY RHINOCEROS OF THE EUROPEAN CAVE PAINTERS

DINOHYUS—*a giant piglike animal*

Pronounced **dy · no · hy · us**

Translated, the word means "terrible hog."

Between 5 and 6 feet tall at the shoulder, and 11 feet in total length.

Lived during Lower Miocene times, 25 million years ago.

Found in the western United States, principally Nebraska.

Full skeletons are displayed at the Carnegie Museum in Pittsburgh; usually only the skull and jaws are shown in other museums.

THIS IS a difficult animal to classify. It is almost, but not exactly, like a pig. Some persons consider it to be one of the ancestors of the pig. Whatever it may have been, Dinohyus is the largest of his kind ever found; the skull of this animal was nearly three feet long. The teeth were strong. In the famous Agate Springs Quarry of Nebraska the teeth and jaws of this animal were particularly numerous.

Pigs are considered successful animals; their fossils are plentiful in all recent periods of time. An older related pig called Archaeotherium was smaller than Dinohyus. It was an Oligocene form whose numerous remains are common in Europe and in western North America. In both of these animals, the teeth show evidence of wear due to a root-eating habit. The skull and lower jaws of both species bore many curious projections. The face was elongated, and the entire head appears to have been out of proportion to the body size.

The peccaries of North and South America are the living descendants of these primitive swine. During the latter part of the ice age very large peccaries were numerous all over North America. Their bones are frequently found in sandy river deposits. The hippopotamus is related to the pigs, and the primitive oreodonts were once thought to be ancestral to all piglike mammals. This notion has since been discarded.

In studying fossil pigs, differences in the skulls of males and females can be confusing. Boars usually have larger heads with a more elaborate development of the canine teeth and grotesque facial projections that were probably covered with stiff bristles.

Skull of Archaeotherium, a pig, 18 inches long

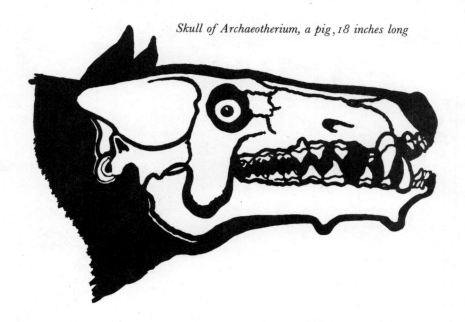

DINOHYUS, THE LARGEST OF THE GIANT PIGS

OREODONT—*the most numerous of the fossil mammals*

Pronounced **o · ree · o · dont**

Translated, the word means "mountain toothed."

*This species—*Merycoidodon culbertsoni—*was the size of a modern sheep, about 3 feet long.*

Lived during Lower Oligocene times, 35 million years ago.

Found in the Bad Lands of South Dakota.

Practically every natural history museum has at least a skull of this animal.

IN THE big Bad Lands of South Dakota there are incredibly extensive beds of oreodont bones. It has been stated that there are more fossils of oreodonts in museums than there are of all other fossil mammal species combined. The animal illustrated is most frequently found.

All oreodonts were of similar appearance, having a piglike body; but each species had a distinctive set of teeth. The even tooth pattern and the internal structure of the teeth lead some to believe that these mammals could have been the ancestors of camels.

During Oligocene times, these mammals traveled in large herds through open forests and river bottom lands. Species that lived later during Pliocene times seem to have developed more aquatic habits.

So many oreodonts have been found and studied that very little of their anatomy is unknown. One interesting feature in the structure of all species from later periods is that the front and hind feet each bore four toes. Only the basic Merycoidodon had five toes on the front feet, an indication of its ancestral position to the entire family. Ordinarily, so numerous a mammal group would be expected to show greater changes in foot structure during a span of more than twenty-five million years.

One species is interesting because cartilage in the larynx had become partially bony and thus was preserved, an indication that the animal must have had tremendous vocal powers.

*Skull of Oreodon culbertsoni,
the most common mammalian
fossil, Oligocene*

74

STENOMYLUS—*called the "gazelle camel"*

Pronounced **steen · o · my · lus**

Translated, the name means "narrow molar."

Was about the size of a large setter.

Lived during Lower Miocene times, about 25 million years ago.

Found in several parts of the western United States.

Displayed in the Denver Museum, the South Dakota School of Mines, the Chicago Museum, the American Museum of Natural History, and many other museums large and small.

THOUGH this animal was clearly related to the camels, it is not exactly like a camel in every detail. It represents one of those peculiar conditions where a series of side issues to a major evolutionary trend developed steadily and then abruptly disappeared, leaving no trace.

Stenomylus was an excellent runner. Its splendid legs terminate in two long, sharp hoofs. This near-camel had no hump. Its most significant structural difference is in the incisor teeth. Based on this difference alone, it is placed in a separate family, of which it is the only representative, distinct from the camels and llamas.

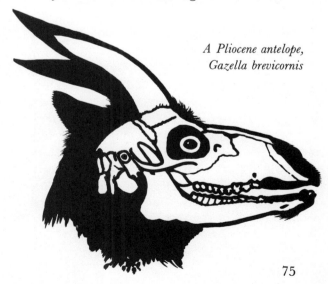

*A Pliocene antelope,
Gazella brevicornis*

75

ALTICAMELUS—*a giraffe camel*

Pronounced **all · tee · ka · *mee* · lus**

Translated, the name means "high camel."

This camel was fully 18 feet tall, the largest of its kind known to date.

Lived during Middle Miocene times, 20 million years ago.

Found in Colorado and other western states.

The finest skeletons are on display at the American Museum of Natural History, New York, and in the University Museum at Lincoln, Nebraska.

JUDGING from the fossil evidence, the camels of the world originated in Asia and migrated into North America. Like the horses, they disappeared from this continent near the close of the ice age. There is no explanation for this disappearance and yet they prospered in this country again after being reintroduced as beasts of burden in the southwestern desert states.

This tremendously tall species fed in open park-like areas. Giraffelike camels such as these are not typical of the family, but they form an interesting offshoot from the main-line trend that produced the living species of Asia and Africa. The elongation of the neck and legs was a unique feature, and both of two toes on each foot bore sharp narrow hoofs. These hoofs are further interesting because until Late Miocene times none of the numerous camel species had yet developed the padded spreading toes that make modern camels unique among the artiodactyls (even-toed, hoofed mammals).

The teeth of camels have slowly evolved from a long even row toward gradual loss of the front teeth and the development of a cropping habit. This method of feeding finds the leaves, twigs, and grass taken by the lips and lower teeth; the food then is precrushed against a tough pad of cartilage on the front of the upper jaw before being ground up by the molars.

During Pliocene times, camels spread all over the world, through Asia, Europe, and South America. Llamas and similar animals of South America are closely related. All species seem to prefer living in open, rather treeless country. The hump and the distinctive stomach chambers seem to especially fit them for living under difficult climatic conditions. The hump serves as a reserve of food, while pockets within the stomach act as water reservoirs.

The spreading feet of camels enable them to walk over loose sand; this particular species of giraffe-camel was the first to show signs of having padded feet. Living camels are of great use to man as beasts of burden and for their ability to endure extremes of weather, both hot and cold. The animal is valued as a transport in places where horses could not live. The hair of the camel is useful in making cloth.

Camels are destructive feeders and are notably short-tempered. A peculiar defensive measure is their habit of spitting and biting. Llamas spit out their entire stomach contents when angry.

Camels have been a distinct mammal group for more than fifty million years. Fossil forms from Eocene times are small, short-legged animals with four toes on the front feet. These earliest forms were hardly larger than rabbits and were quite similar in structure to the oreodonts of that period.

Samotherium, a Pliocene giraffe, length 24 inches

ALTICAMELUS, A GIANT GIRAFFE CAMEL

PROTOCERAS—*a deerlike hoofed mammal*

Pronounced **pro · tow · *sair* · us**

Translated, the name means "first deer."

Was the size of a large modern sheep.

Lived from Upper Eocene times until Lower Pliocene times, 50 until 10 million years ago.

Found principally in areas that were once plains; Nebraska has produced the finest skeletons.

Usually the skull is the only body part displayed. The University of Princeton Museum and the University of Nebraska Museum have unusually fine collections.

THE FAMILY to which this animal belongs comprises the most unusual and rare members of the deer family. Generally the Protoceridae are small animals whose skulls and feet make them difficult to classify. Some species were the size of an ordinary rabbit; the largest individuals seldom exceeded the size of a sheep. They had large heads and short legs.

The skulls of male animals have been the most frequent evidence found. These are unique because of their peculiar horn structure. There were no true antlers; the horny core of the skull projections must have been covered with skin rather than a sheath of harder material. Very little is known of the female animals, but it is probable that they had no horns at all. The canine teeth of the males were abnormally long and projected well below the lower lip. These fangs were sharp and were undoubtedly used during annual fights for leadership of the herd.

The feet of these animals are peculiar because those in front often had four exposed toes, each bearing a small hoof. The hind feet were most often two-toed and internally more modern in structure. This strange difference between the front and hind feet is further accentuated by the length of the legs. Skeletons would seem to indicate that the rear portions of the body were carried much lower than the shoulders, almost as though the animal were in a continual crouch. Some authorities therefore would like to link these animals with the oreodonts and the peculiar gazelle-camel, Stenomylus.

There are four different kinds of deerlike mammals quite similar to the Protoceras group that are lumped together under the term *traguloids* by some authorities. These four divisions include the early traguloids themselves, very rare animals best known from Lower Oligocene times; second, the *hypertragulids;* third, the Protoceras types illustrated here; and finally, the *tragulids,* which apparently gave rise to the modern deer. In all four of these divisions, the chief differences between the individual animals can be seen best in the feet and in the teeth.

None of the animals within these groups are numerous as fossils, therefore it is likely that complete analysis of their relationships will remain doubtful for a long time. In Africa and in parts of Asia there is a small deerlike animal called the chevrotain, whose scientific name is *Tragulis.* This is perhaps the only living link to the fossil forms previously described. The chevrotain, or mouse-deer, is a very small animal; it has as many rodent features within the body as it has features of the deer family.

It is supposed that the hornlike growths on the skulls of the protocerids helped them to survive for a fairly long time. The growths that appeared on the front portion of the face were distinctive and probably most useful as defensive weapons. These same forward projections raise a doubt about the exact relationship of this group to the deer, for the kind of horny growths found on the skulls of these two groups are strikingly different.

Most of the remains of this animal come from Nebraska and Texas. Present excavating activity is turning up more and more bone material that may help paleontologists understand the animals. The front feet are, for some reason, scarce as fossils, and skeletons of the females are needed to round out the knowledge of the family.

Protoceras, from South Dakota

(Not all drawn to same scale)

Syndyoceras, from Nebraska

Prosynthetoceras, from Texas

PROTOCERATIDS,

STRANGE DEERLIKE MAMMALS

VARIOUS SPECIES OF DEER

Deer range from 15 inches in height to giants well over 6 feet tall at the shoulders. The average is probably near 3½ feet at the shoulders.

The deer family had its origins during Miocene times, approximately 20 million years ago.

Fossils are encountered literally anywhere; more recent species are often known from archeological sites.

Not many natural history museums display fossil deer but rely instead upon mounted modern forms to typify the entire family.

AMONG fossil mammals the deer family is a recent one. Its origins seem to lie in eastern Europe and Asia. Members of this varied group migrated into North America rather late in our geologic history, and a great many of these species became extinct towards the close of the Pleistocene. The true deer apparently began to develop as a separate mammal line during Miocene times.

The most obvious difference between deer species lies in the type of antlers grown by the males and in the proportions of the legs. The antlers of the males are unique among mammals because of their method of growth and the fact that they are dropped annually just after the breeding season. The battles that occur between rival males are fearful demonstrations of strength, but they are seldom fatal to the individuals. This struggle for leadership of a small band of deer is characteristic of the family; it is a habit not shared by most of the other horned mammals.

The antlers that are dropped each year deteriorate rapidly and are seldom preserved as fossils. Females of very few species bear antlers, and it is therefore of some concern to those who classify them that careful identification is made. Male deer are often much larger than the females, and because of such differences it might be possible to find the skull of a female and think it to be something new and previously unidentified.

There are basically three kinds of animals classed within the deer or cervid group. One is the palaeomerycids, which show primitive structural similarities to both giraffes and deer. Apparently they had no antlers, their legs were essentially modern, and both males and females had long canine teeth. There is a modern survivor of this group in the musk deer of central Asia. This linking of the fossil and the living species is, however, doubted by some authorities.

The second large division within the deer family includes all of the true deer that grow antlers.

The third major division includes the giraffes. The living species of Africa appears to be the tallest of these, sometimes growing fully eighteen feet tall. The giraffes are apparently the tropical country counterpart of the antlered deer. As with the true deer, there has been considerable variation in the size and shape of their skin-covered horns. These have never been shed though at one time they grew in some species to considerable size. The horns have varied greatly from species to species in number and distribution over the entire surface of the skull. The okapi, which was discovered in the Belgian Congo of Africa in 1900, is in every sense a living fossil from this giraffe group; its bones can scarcely be distinguished from fossil forms that are known from Late Pliocene times.

The entire deer family is placed in the group of animals known as artiodactyls (even-toed, hoofed mammals). Deer are browsers, feeding on twigs and similar coarse food. The earlier ancestors of the group generally had four toes on each foot, and the tooth pattern was a general one, consisting of a full set of forty-four teeth not adapted to one single kind of feeding habit. Deer are among the few kinds of mammals that have done well in competition with man during modern times.

Parablastomeryx, a Miocene ancestor of deer and giraffes, length 14 inches

HEADS OF UNUSUAL NORTH AMERICAN DEER

(not all drawn to same scale)

Lull's deerlet,
from Nebraska

Douglass' deer,
from Nebraska

Rak's deer,
from California

Sinclair's deer,
from Nebraska

Gregory's deerlet,
from Nebraska

Procranioceras,
from Nebraska

Cranioceras,
from Nebraska

Sinclairomeryx,
from Nebraska

CERVALCES—*an ice age moose*

Pronounced **serv · al · seez**

Translated, the name means "deerlike moose."

The same size as the living moose.

Lived during Late Pleistocene times and until 15,000 years ago.

Found in New Jersey and Alaska.

The finest specimen is displayed in the museum at the University of Princeton.

THIS IS a rather rare animal. Until recently it was known from only a single specimen. Placer-mining operations in Alaska have since uncovered a wide variety of extinct mammal parts, and among them have been very fragmentary remains of this moose and a related species that was considerably larger.

Cervalces had the wide-spreading hoofs and the long legs of a moose. This is taken as evidence that the animal lived in a habitat of deep snows or water. The skull was not typically mooselike; the nose was not as large as that of the living varieties, and the antlers were narrower.

The fossils of some deer are difficult to interpret because the females did not have antlers. Much preserved material in museums consists of skull fragments and pieces of antler. The more delicate leg and body bones were apparently scattered and destroyed quickly after death. Working with head parts leaves room for doubt as to proper identification, since the skull portions may be those of a female of a species already described from an antlered specimen.

The deer that have lived in North America are divided into six families; these are further divided into many individual species. The reason for the disappearance of most of them from North America following the retreat of the glaciers remains a puzzle.

Fossil specimens are not much different from living types; cold and food shortages could not have killed off so many species. It is a widely held notion that disease transmitted by insects may have killed many of the largest ice age mammals, among them deerlike Cervalces.

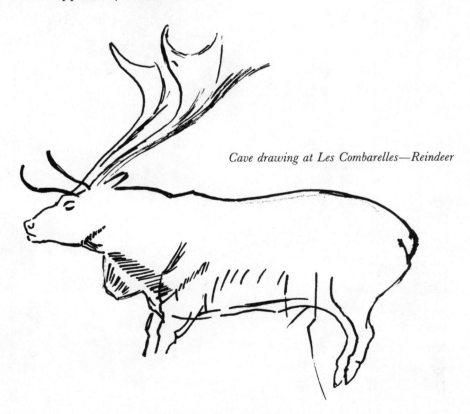

Cave drawing at Les Combarelles—Reindeer

82

CERVALCES, A PLEISTOCENE MOOSE

MEGACEROS—*a giant deer, more commonly called the Irish elk*

Pronounced **mee · gas · er · us**

Translated, the name means "great-horned."

Antler spread was about 10 feet; the body was sturdy and just under 6 feet high at the shoulders.

Lived during Late Pleistocene times, and until only a few thousand years ago.

Found principally in Irish bogs.

Displayed in nearly every large museum.

IN EUROPE and in North America, two members of the deer family grew to truly gigantic proportions. Megaceros was the European giant; its more common name is the Irish elk, simply because its remains have been found most frequently in that country. In our own country the largest individual deer was a variety of the giant moose Cervalces.

The antlers of Megaceros are the largest known from any deer. Some antler specimens spread to nearly ten feet and were nearly four inches thick. Tremendous weight is supposed to have been one of the contributing factors to this mammal's eventual disappearance. Some persons feel that the weight of the antlers overbalanced Megaceros when it leaned forward to drink. Since so many of the known skeletons have come from bogs, it is assumed that once an animal of this size fell into such a bog it could not escape and eventually died there.

Primitive man also contributed to the downfall of this species. There are many records of its bones and antler pieces being found in close association with the artifacts of early man in the British Isles. These show that tools and weapons were made from the bones of this deer and that it was a staple part of the diet. One popular illustration shows a group of men pursuing a swimming Irish elk across an open lake. This is exactly the kind of animal that would have been wiped out by the earliest hunters, for the excessive antler size of the males must have been a terrible handicap during a chase.

Not too long ago there was a great demand for the skeleton of this animal. Newly founded American museums were most anxious to acquire spectacular specimens, and the European sources were able to provide them by reopening bogs that were previous sources of skeletons. These bogs were systematically drained, and all available specimens of the Irish elk were collected. The acid bog-water preserved such bones beautifully, and the immense antlers were particularly fortunate finds since they are otherwise seldom preserved.

Antlers of the Irish elk

Female Megaceros

MEGACEROS, A GREAT DEER WITH A RECORD ANTLER SPREAD

ANTILOCAPRID—*a primitive antelope*

Pronounced an · till · o · *cap* · rid

Translated, the name means "goatlike antelope."

Generally no larger than living goats, but with longer legs.

Lived during Upper Miocene times, 15 million years ago, and until the present.

Found throughout the western Plains regions.

Full skeletons displayed in the Chicago Natural History Museum, the Denver Natural History Museum, the Carnegie Museum in Pittsburgh, and in similar large paleontological collections.

PRACTICALLY ALL of the known mammals grouped as antilocaprids come from North America. They were apparently numerous, though their skeletons are not common as fossils. Antilocaprids sprang away from the main line of bovine evolution in Early Miocene times and exist today in a single living species, the prong-horned antelope of western North America.

Antelopes are related to cattle in many ways, but they differ greatly in over-all size and external appearance. Most individuals are no longer than the average goat, but they are particularly well adapted to swift running and life in an open near-desert habitat. These are grazing animals with strong teeth well adapted to grinding.

The horns of antilocaprids are of interest because they contain a horn core of bone that is never shed. The external covering of the horn is shed annually. It is in the horns that the greatest variety among species occurs. The living form of North America, though unique, is but a modest representative of this once numerous group. Extinct species had horns that were quite elaborate.

The antilocaprids are divided into two groups. One contains the merycodonts, which were for the most part very small mammals. These were to the North American plains the same kind of animal that thrives today on grassy African plains. The second group were the antilocaprini. Members of this latter group are rare, and their remains appear only in late geological horizons. The former division is typified by skull projections that tend to branch as a deer's antlers branch; the latter group had simpler horns tending to twist and curve backward.

The feet of most antilocaprids are of modern structure, having completely lost the side toes. The teeth, too, are essentially modern. None of the anatomical features of the individual species varied a great deal from those of other species within the classification. The entire skeleton was rather uniform; the heads of the male animals were distinctive, and the females had horns that were much less conspicuous. The beards of the goatlike mammals were a further mark of distinction among the males.

These animals shared with goats and related forms the peculiarity of using musk glands as a means of identifying themselves, their herds, and their home territories.

It has been assumed that these animals originated in Asia along with cattle and migrated to this continent during Miocene times.

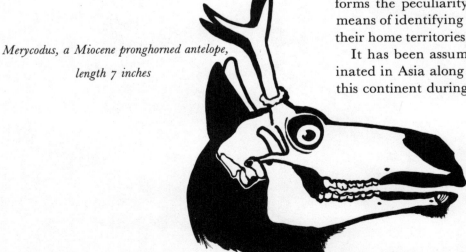

Merycodus, a Miocene pronghorned antelope,

length 7 inches

HEADS OF NORTH AMERICAN PRONGLETS

5 species are of the Merycodontini division, 1 species is of the
Antilocaprini division (not all drawn to the same scale)

Ramoceros,
from New Mexico

Paramoceros,
from New Mexico

Subparacosoryx,
from Nebraska

Paracosoryx,
from Nebraska

Merriam's pronglet,
from California

Osborn's pronghorn,
from New Mexico

HEADS OF NORTH AMERICAN PRONGBUCKS
the division called the Antilocaprini
(not all drawn to the same scale)

The prepronghorn, Plioceros

Quentin's pronghorn, Stockoceros

Hay's pronghorn, Hayoceros

The spiraled pronghorn, Ilingoceros

DROMOMERYX—*the first antelope*

Pronounced **dro · mo · *mare* · ix**

Translated, the name means "running ruminant."

This animal was the size of a small goat.

Lived during Middle Miocene times, 20 million years ago.

Found in Nebraska, Montana, and Colorado.

Skeletons are displayed in the University of Princeton Museum and the Carnegie Museum in Pittsburgh. Skeletal material is owned by many other museums.

PRIOR TO Miocene times, deerlike animals were small and often hornless. Dromomeryx was the first of the larger deer to mark a change in that family's status in North America. Cud-chewing mammals had been heavy-bodied, short-legged beasts. In this first antelope, the body was still rather heavy, but the legs were slender and had become efficient running mechanisms.

The straight horns of this animal suggest that it may have been the forerunner of the modern antelope that lives in our western states. These horns were not shed and look very much like the simple skin-covered growths on the head of the giraffe. This is only one of the points that makes decisive classification of the animal doubtful.

The living American pronghorned antelope, perhaps the most unusual North American mammal

89

BISON—*related to modern cattle, often called the buffalo*

Pronounced **by · son**

Translated, the name means "wild ox."

Some species are known only from skulls or horn cores; these are difficult to know fully. The modern forms are generally 11 feet long and weigh well over 1,000 pounds.

Most species lived during the most recent million years of the earth's history.

Found almost any place where recent fossils are found, particularly near former watering places and salt licks.

Usually the skulls alone are displayed. Full skeletons are shown in the Denver Museum, Los Angeles County Museum, and similar large museums.

BISON, sheep, and the musk ox are the only representatives of their family in North America. All of these mammals are of apparently recent origin, and relatively few fossils of their remains are known from periods older than the Pleistocene.

The bison is the only member of the cattle family—the bovids—known to have been native to the area now the United States. Recent field work has revealed at least one new species from Alaska. Such animals migrated as far south as El Salvador in Central America, but none ever lived in South America until introduced by man in modern times.

The Plains Indians that lived upon the bison herds apparently did not understand the possibilities of using the milk of these animals as food. Primitive peoples in other parts of the world had long since discovered the value of this food source from many of the hoofed animals closely related to the North American bison.

Because these mammals are such a recent addition to our North American fauna, total skeletons of extinct forms are seldom found. Many specimens have been described from skulls, horn cores, and only the most massive portions of the other bones in the skeleton. Most of these fossil remains are found very close to the surface, and as we have noted specimens lying in place just below the surface begin to disintegrate while still buried. By the time erosion has exposed the bone it has broken up into tiny bits. It will take considerable new collecting from well-known localities to gather a sufficiently large series to permit accurate classification of the several species of North American bison.

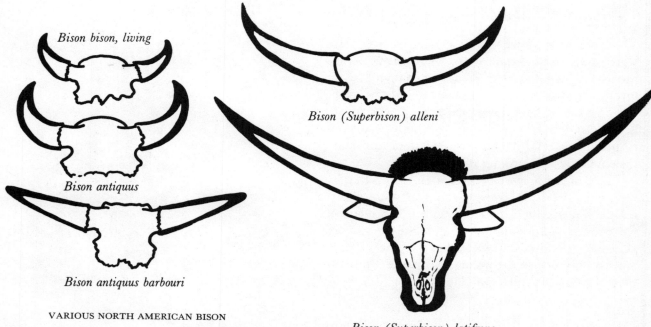

Bison bison, living

Bison antiquus

Bison antiquus barbouri

Bison (Superbison) alleni

Bison (Superbison) latifrons

VARIOUS NORTH AMERICAN BISON

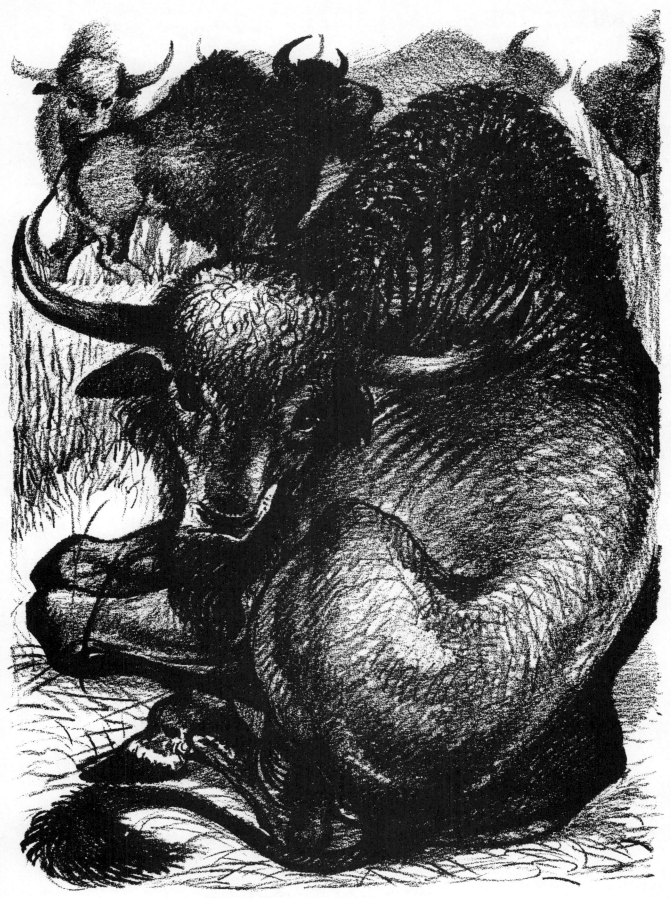

ONE OF THE MANY BISON OF THE AMERICAN ICE AGE

VARIOUS HORNED MAMMALS
KNOWN AS FOSSILS

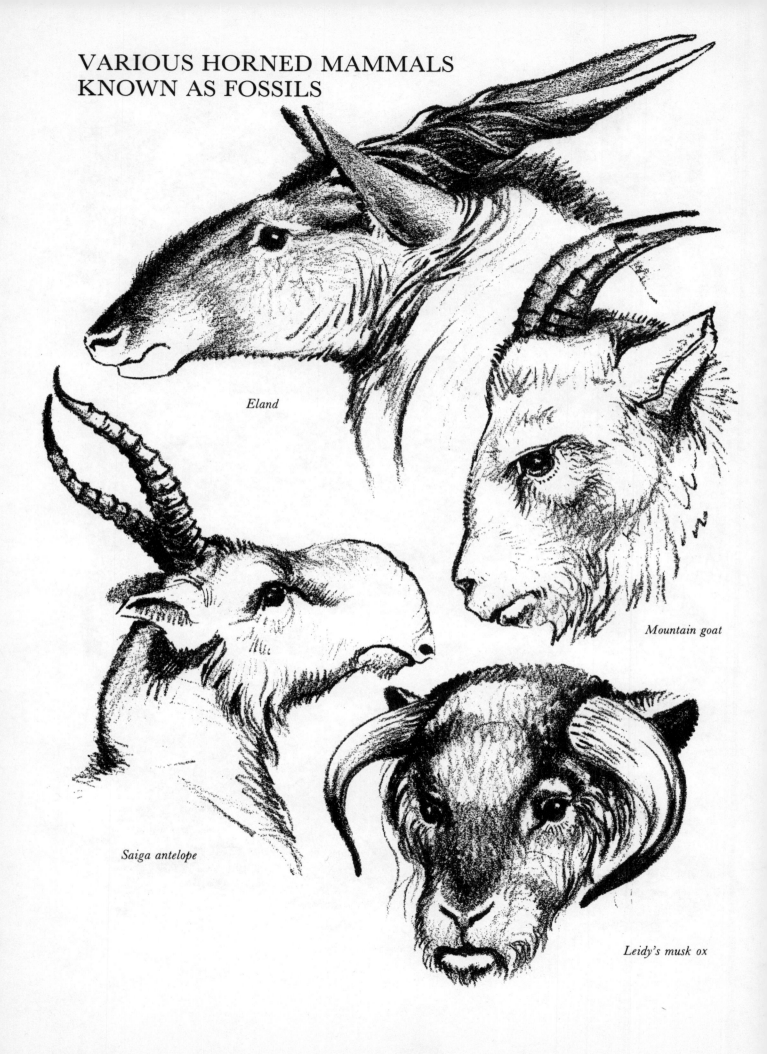

Eland

Mountain goat

Saiga antelope

Leidy's musk ox

MUSK OX—*an arctic mammal of recent origin*

The name is derived from the animal's heavy, musky odor.

About the size of a cow, but with shorter legs and with long, shaggy hair.

Lived during Pleistocene times and until the present, a span of less than a million years.

Found in many scattered localities all over the Northern Hemisphere.

Fossils not generally displayed in United States museums; mounted modern forms are usually representative for the group.

THIS IS a modern mammal, related to the sheep and the antelopes; it still lives in arctic countries. Musk oxen were a distinguishing feature of the Pleistocene fauna of North America, Europe, and Asia. Nothing is known of the origins of this species, for the fossil records of their kind do not go beyond the ice age. It seems logical to assume from the evidence that the group as a whole may have originated in Asia and migrated to the east and west.

There are very few kinds of fossil musk oxen known, and these do not vary in size to a great degree. The living form from arctic North America is very slightly larger than any of the fossil species.

The living musk ox travels and feeds in small herds; the members of the band defend themselves vigorously when attacked. It is the habit of the adults to form a defensive ring with the individuals facing outward, offering a solid front of sharp horns to wolves or an occasional polar bear.

Men have no trouble killing the musk ox, and there is great danger that the species will be completely exterminated in the near future. The survival of this animal under severe arctic conditions should throw interesting light on the survival ability of other Pleistocene species.

WILD CATTLE—*a key to the success of man*

Living and extinct cattle are generally the same over-all size, but modern types usually have shorter legs and horns.

Many cattle now extinct flourished during Pliocene and Pleistocene times, a span of 10 million years.

On this continent the cattle are represented by the bison and rare Alaskan finds of a yak-like animal.

Many museums display modern bison to typify the bovid mammals.

THE CATTLE are the world's most numerous and successful living hoofed mammals. There are more than a hundred known genera, animals without which human beings would be hard pressed to feed their growing populations.

These mammals are typified by hollow horns on both the males and females. These are not shed during the animal's lifetime. Their feet are of modern structure. Their stomach is divided into the four chambers typical of the cud-chewers.

Domestication of these animals, early in man's history, was an important step forward to civilization. The fact that cows are able to convert grass into edible milk and meat, and the animal's gentle nature and adaptability to breeding for size and greater milk production, makes them ideal servants to man.

The humpless form of cattle we know best prob-

ably is descended from a European species called *Bos primigenius*. This animal was a long-horned variety whose likeness appears in many of the early cave drawings discovered in Europe.

The cattle remains found in archaeological sites are those of rather small species. It was at one time argued that primitive man caught and tamed larger animals and then bred them to a smaller size. This argument has been set aside, since it can be demonstrated that large animals that are bred to become smaller usually retain full-sized teeth almost unchanged. In the case of the dwarf species of prehistoric times, both the teeth and the bones are uniformly small. This would seem to indicate that early hunters deliberately sought the smallest, more controllable animals for domestication. The yak and the buffalo of Asia and Africa are the nearest thing to wild cattle alive today.

94

MIACIS—*the ancestor of modern carnivores*
Pronounced **my · *ack* · is**

Translated, the name means "small pointed," referring to the sharp teeth.

Was about the size of a large squirrel.

Lived during Eocene times, 50 million years ago.

Found in a very few scattered localities in several western states.

Full skeletons have not been found; fossils are seldom displayed.

THIS ANIMAL is generally acknowledged to be the ancestor of all living carnivores. Miacis was a long step from the large heavy-headed creodonts. Perhaps its most significant feature was a relatively larger brain.

Though a small mammal, this single species shows points of structure that relate it to the cats, civets, weasels, and dogs. One of the important points is a change in tooth pattern away from that of the creodonts and toward what we consider a typically carnivorous one.

Fossil remains of this mammal are rare, and incomplete when they are found, probably because Miacis must have spent much of its time in the trees. The feet had five toes, each bearing a sharp-pointed claw that was probably retractable, an aid to climbing and capturing quick-moving prey.

The bodily appearance of Miacis suggests that its hunting movements may have been like those of the modern weasel. The head, body, and tail are all long, and the legs are short. In total structure this species was sufficiently primitive to be ancestral to both the cats and dogs without being essentially either one.

Until a complete skeleton is found, it is impossible to say what path of evolution the descendants of this animal followed. That the early history of the cat family is uncertain is probably a result of the tree-climbing habit we suppose them to have had. Many paleontologists feel that the cats originated in central Asia and spread over the rest of the world very swiftly.

DINICTIS—*a form ancestral to the biting cats*

Pronounced **dy · *nick* · tis**

Translated, the name means "terrible stabber."

This animal was about 3½ feet long.

Lived during Oligocene times, 35 million years ago.

Found in the Dakota Bad Lands, and in similar localities in several western states.

At least the skull is a common museum specimen all over this country.

ALL THE CATS are divided into two groups: the stabbing cats, including all of the saber-toothed species, and the biting cats, best typified by the modern tiger. Dinictis is a puzzle to paleontologists because it shows some relationship to both of these major divisions of the cat family. The skull structure is a mixture of each.

The skeleton of Dinictis shows him to have been short-legged and long-bodied. In this respect, the animal was a typical primitive carnivore. It is in the skull and feet that the cat characteristics show most clearly.

The early fossil record of the biting cats is rather incomplete. They reached a peak during the ice age, when great lions roamed over practically all of the great land masses except Australia. There are many representatives of the group alive today.

In contrast, the fossil record of the stabbing cats is a fairly continuous one from the time of Dinictis until roughly 5,000 years ago. But there are no living descendants of this once numerous group of animals.

These two types of cats shared the same kind of habitats to some extent, but they did not hunt and kill their prey in the same way.

This animal's skeleton is found quite frequently in association with the oreodonts of the Oligocene. Most often these deposits suggest that the animals whose fossils are found within them spent considerable time near the broad rivers of the open western plains.

Dinictis was not very specialized as a predator, but carnivore competition at that time was neither numerous nor strong. This cat was probably the most formidable predatory Oligocene mammal.

TOP—HOPLOPHONEUS, A SABER-TOOTHED CAT OF THE OLIGOCENE
BOTTOM—DINICTIS, AN EARLY TRUE CAT OF THE OLIGOCENE

SMILODON—*the saber-toothed cat from the tar pits*

Pronounced **smy · low · don**

Translated, the name means "carving-knife tooth."

Shorter than a modern lion, but of heavier build. The fangs were 9 inches long.

This type of cat lived from Oligocene times until 8,000 years ago.

Best known from the tar pits at Hancock Park, Los Angeles, California.

Spectacular mountings have been loaned to nearly every large museum in this country by the Los Angeles County Museum.

THIS ANIMAL is frequently referred to as a tiger, but there is nothing in its skeletal structure to warrant the name tiger. Smilodon was the largest of its kind; the spectacular canine teeth that have given it its name were fully nine inches long and bore fine serrations along the cutting edge.

The saber-toothed cats have a history thirty-five million years long. They seem to have originated in Asia and spread over much of the world. In this country they died out during Pleistocene times and left no living trace. In Europe a species of saber-tooth nearly as large as Smilodon existed until the end of Pleistocene times and was well known to primitive man.

Structurally these great cats were marvelously adapted as killers. They had short muscular legs and powerful shoulders that enabled them to cling to their prey. The neck was short and muscular. The fangs were used to stab and slash. The lower jaw could open so wide that it was completely out of the way during the animal's attack. The nose was large and had moved slightly backward in the skull to permit the cat to breathe while its face was buried deep in the thick fur of its prey.

From the tooth pattern, it is difficult to see how these cats were able to chew well, if at all. Some authorities feel that they might have lived on blood alone, or perhaps gulped chunks of meat after slashing them from their victims' bodies.

Smilodon had a short bobtail, and its muscular body was shorter than that of the other large lions that were its contemporaries. The most complete skeletons of this animal have come from the tar pits at Rancho La Brea in California. These pits have yielded literally thousands of specimens that represent every stage of development from tiny cub to sick and old individuals.

The remains of similar saber-toothed species are known from nearly every part of the United States. Many of them have been found in western caves. There was a smaller saber-toothed cat that lived in Oligocene times, thirty-five million years ago. It had a long tail and was built like a leopard. Its sabers were more needlelike than the flat fangs of Smilodon. The name of this animal was Hoplophoneus, meaning "armed killer."

These were among the most unusual animals of the entire sixty million years of the Age of Mammals.

SMILODON, THE EPITOME OF CARNIVORE SPECIALIZATION

FELIS ATROX—*a giant lion*

Pronounced **feel** · is **ay** · **trox**

Translated, the name means "fierce cat," felis being the generic name for the cats.

This lion was about ⅓ larger than living species.

Lived during the ice age and until approximately 8,000 years ago.

Found in many scattered localities all over the United States; the type specimen came from Natchez, Mississippi.

Finest displays are at the Los Angeles County Museum.

BIG CATS range far in hunting their food. They live and die in open country. Except for deposits like the famous tar pits of California, their fossil remains are scattered and rather rare.

Smilodon was the largest saber-toothed cat; this lion lived at the same time and was an even larger animal. Though their habits of feeding must have been strikingly different, both great cats shared the same habitat to some extent.

While the tar pits have yielded thousands of saber-toothed specimens, there have been relatively few giant lions found. The ratio of skeletons discovered is roughly 30 to 1. From their longer legs and greater stature it is assumed that these lions pursued their prey vigorously rather than leaping on the victim, slashing it, and clinging to it while it bled to death from the wound.

The teeth of this lion are typically feline, well adapted to both chewing and shearing flesh. Though the skull and skeleton are considerably larger than that of the modern lion, the basic structural details are very similar.

This animal had a long tail and a mane. The mane was kept short by the tangled thorns and brush of the plains country. In some ways this lion was like the South American jaguar, but from the length of its legs it can be concluded that it did not readily climb trees.

It has been suggested that the giant saber-toothed cats died out because, to some extent, they killed off their own food supply. The giant lion also died out of the American and European fauna during these same Pleistocene times. It seems too much of a coincidence that the great predators and herbivores could have disappeared so completely and at the same moment in history without a drastic change of weather or a widespread disease being the cause.

Saber-toothed cats fed heavily on giant sloths, mastodons, and other tough-skinned, long-haired mammals. The giant lion fed on the hoofed mammals such as the bison, antelopes, and horses. Many lion remains are discovered in rocky places throughout the western United States. These spots overlook what must have been rich hunting grounds.

FELIS ATROX, THE GIANT LION OF WESTERN NORTH AMERICA

CYNODICTIS—*a primitive dog*

Pronounced **sigh · no · *dick* · tis**

Translated, the name means "dog stabber," a reference to its needle-sharp canine teeth.

Was the size of a small modern fox.

Lived during Lower Oligocene times, 35 million years ago.

Found in South Dakota, Wyoming, and a few scattered localities in other western states.

Full skeletons are rare and not generally displayed.

THE EARLY HISTORY of all carnivorous mammal types is represented by several species that outwardly resemble Cynodictis. In a relatively few million years mammals such as these have increased in size considerably, but internally their bodies have not changed much from a basic miacid stock.

This doglike mammal seems to have given rise to more than fifty similar species during Oligocene times. Most of these show a definite tendency to become more and more doglike. During this early stage of their development, these dogs had not yet shown skeletal changes toward their present strong running habit.

Earliest dog types had long flexible bodies and short legs. The feet had five toes and retractable claws. The molar teeth had begun to disappear and in their place the remaining teeth became more specialized for the flesh-eating habit.

Cynodictis is the perfect picture of progress and a good illustration of an intermediate mammal that will lead into a more specialized line of evolution.

The land carnivores of the world are divided into two major groups: the aeluroids, including civets, hyenas, and cats; and the arctoids, including dogs, bears, raccoons, and weasels. Both groups are further classed as fissipeds, carnivores that dwell on the land and have toes that are separated. The aquatic carnivores, like the seal and walrus, are called pinnipeds, a term meaning "fin-footed."

DAPHOENODON—*ancestor of the bears and modern dogs*

Pronounced daf · *een* · o · don

Translated, the name means "bloody tooth."

Was slightly larger than a modern coyote, about 4 to 5 feet in total length.

Lived in Lower Miocene times, about 25 million years ago.

Found in Wyoming and other western states.

Skulls are displayed in many museums. There is a fine skeleton at the Carnegie Museum in Pittsburgh.

THIS ANIMAL represents a transition from the primitive catlike Miacis to the ancestral dogs. In the skull there are many structures which make the animal appear doglike, but in the feet, the hind legs, and the vertebrae of the lower back, Daphoendon resembles a primitive cat.

The large vertebrae mentioned above indicate strong muscles in the hindquarters, and these in turn would indicate the ability to leap powerfully, as a large cat of today would leap to catch its prey.

Daphoenodon was one of the largest predators of his time. Later less specialized Miocene forms grew twice as large. This was not, as some scientists first thought, a completely bearlike dog. Bears walk flat-footed; this animal walked on its toes. As in all of the "bear dogs," the feet make

the animal hard to classify. Its feet were catlike early in their evolution, and this character persisted through long periods of change in other characteristics.

Daphoenodon had a long wolflike head, a long low-slung body, long tail, and short powerful legs with spreading toes on the feet. In outward appearance, the creature resembled earlier flesh-eating creodont mammals.

Many of the known skeletons of this mammal come from Upper Oligocene and Lower Miocene deposits. Though considered to be primitive forms, the teeth of Daphoenodon changed from the basic miacid pattern, which was purely carnivorous, to a pattern that showed some tendency toward a varied diet more like that of the bears and dogs.

CAVE BEAR—*a contemporary of man*

Scientific name: Ursus spelaeus, *ursus meaning "bear," and spelaeus "cave." Pronounced* **ur · sus spee · *lee* · us**

Was about 4 feet high at the shoulder when on all fours, 6 to 7 feet when standing erect in a defensive posture.

Many related forms all lived between 15,000 and 5,000 years ago.

Remains are found in European caves.

Seldom displayed in our museums since most remains are fragmentary.

BEARS are a recent development in mammal history. Their family dates back only twenty-five million years, into Miocene times. Bears are the close relatives of dogs and raccoons; their direct line of descent into the past shows them diverging from dog ancestry. They are obviously distinguished from dogs by their great size and flat feet and their willingness to eat virtually anything.

The cave bear is best known from Europe. He gets his common and scientific name from the fact that his remains are most frequently found in caves, particularly those that also show signs of having been used by prehistoric human beings. There is a great deal of evidence to indicate that primitive man hunted this bear successfully.

Most species of bear are confined to the northern countries of the world, though one type is found in the northern parts of tropical Africa. Though cave bears were large, none of them exceeded the stature of living Alaskan brown bears. Several prehistoric bears had unusually large heads, and a few species had unusually short snouts. These North and South American species of short-faced bears were called Arctotherium.

The entire bear family walks flat-footed. Their most distinguishing anatomical feature is a tooth pattern and structure that indicates a primarily vegetable diet. All bears are strong animals; their claws are not retractable but can be used skillfully for digging and handling incredibly small insects and similar food.

The disposition of any bear is unpredictable, and a large individual would have been a tough quarry for any primitive hunter. Early man cherished bear claws as an ornament; they might well have been a badge of courage that distinguished the hunters.

THE CAVE BEAR AND CUBS, A COMMON EUROPEAN SPECIES

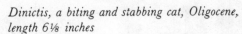
Dinictis, a biting and stabbing cat, Oligocene, length 6⅛ inches

Smilodon, the greatest of the stabbing cats, Pleistocene, length 12 inches

SKULLS OF BITING AND STABBING CATS

Hoplophoneus, an early stabbing cat, Oligocene, length 6¼ inches

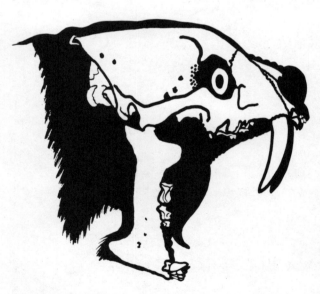

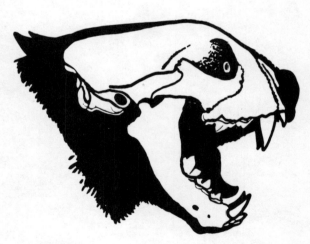

Metailurus, a true cat, Pliocene, length 5¾ inches

DIRE WOLF—*a nearly modern wolf*

A self-explanatory name, chosen because of the animal's ominous size and great numbers.

This wolf was slightly larger than any other species found within the United States.

Lived during Pleistocene times and died out approximately 10,000 years ago.

Fossils are found all over the United States; they are most numerous from the tar pits of California.

The finest collection of specimens is in the Los Angeles County Museum.

THIS WOLF, though not much longer than modern species, had a stockier build and a larger head. Its teeth and jaws were strong; the size of the skull and shoulders seems to indicate that a considerable part of the animal's diet was carrion rather than prey killed in active pursuit. The La Brea tar pits have yielded thousands of individual specimens representing all ages and states of health. The skeletons of the tar-pit wolf outnumber those of any other mammal from that famous collecting locality. This would seem to bear out the contention that these were not active wolves but that they preferred to harass large concentrations of animals that could be captured easily.

Throughout the United States, the remains of other similar wolves are often found in association with mammals that lived in open country. The tremendous buffalo herds seem to have been the most favored source of food. Larger timber wolves are known from Canada and the most gigantic of all the dog family is an Asiatic species that also lived during postglacial times.

The skull and teeth of this wolf well typify the structural features of all carnivorous mammals. The serious student of paleontology uses this skull as reference in learning the proper names and relationships of the bones and teeth in the mammalian skull.

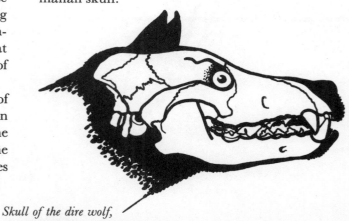

Skull of the dire wolf, typical of mammalian carnivores

CHART OF CARNIVORE EVOLUTION

Walrus

Earless seals

Eared seals

Raccoons

Bears

Dogs

Weasels, skunks

Civets

Hyenas

Cats

PINNIPEDS
(FIN-FOOTED)

ARCTOIDS (BEARLIKE)

Pliocene epoch

Miocene epoch

Hyaenodonts

AELUROIDS (CATLIKE)

Bear dog

Oligocene epoch

Oxyaenodonts

Mesonychids

Arctocyonids

FISSIPEDS (SEPARATED TOES)

Eocene epoch

Miacids

CREODONTS
(FLESH-EATING TEETH)

Paleocene epoch

CERATOGAULUS—*an unusual rodent*

Pronounced **sair · a · tow · gawl · us**

Translated, the name means "horned digger."

Was about 2 feet long.

Lived during Pliocene times approximately 10 million years ago.

Found principally in Nebraska.

Skeletons at the University of Nebraska Museum and at the Smithsonian Institution in Washington, D. C.

THE HORNS of this large rodent are a riddle to scientists. As a rule, such animals are burrowers and quite shy in habit. The horns of this species may have been present on the males alone, but the record is not clear in this respect.

The oldest known fossil of a mammal is that of a rodentlike form from Jurassic times, but there is no strong line of fossil evidence between those distant animals and the true rodents of the later Cenozoic Era. Rodent remains are numerous enough, but they are so varied and in some cases so fragmentary that there is no agreement among scientists as to their classification.

Fossil rodents can be generally divided into three large arbitrary groups. These are typified as a whole by (*a*) squirrels, (*b*) rats, and (*c*) porcupines. Rabbits and hares are distinctive enough to be classified by themselves as Lagomorphs, from the Greek words for "hare" and "form." Apart from the teeth alone, their body structures offer no link to the rodents. They have existed as a distinct group for sixty million years.

One of the most interesting fossils we know of is that of a solid, mud-filled rodent's burrow. When discovered it was called a "devil's corkscrew," because the main passage from the surface to the living quarters was a very regular, evenly spiraled tube that looked like a corkscrew. Entire colonies of these burrows were discovered in Nebraska. They were at first thought to be tree roots; many years later they were properly identified.

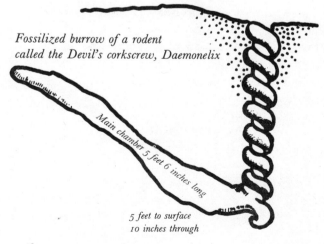

Fossilized burrow of a rodent called the Devil's corkscrew, Daemonelix

Main chamber 5 feet 6 inches long

5 feet to surface
10 inches through

CASTOROIDES—*a beaver as large as a bear*

Pronounced **cass · tow · roy · deez**

Translated, the name means "formed like a beaver," from castor "beaver" and oides, "form."

Was nearly 10 feet long including the 3-foot tail.

Beavers are known from Oligocene times, 35 million years ago. This species lived only 10,000 years ago.

Found in Ohio, Illinois, Alaska, and scattered localities throughout the eastern United States.

Seldom displayed in museums since most remains are quite fragmentary.

THIS spectacular rodent attained a total length of nearly ten feet. Castoroides shared the habitat of the mastodon, the giant sloth, and many other ice age giants. Its remains turn up in scattered localities from Alaska to Florida, but the major number of specimens are recorded from states near the Great Lakes.

The rodents and the even-toed hoofed mammals are the most successful of all living mammals. As in the case of the hoofed mammals, rodents are difficult to classify because they are numerous and only slightly different from each other. The major skeletal changes occur in the chewing mechanism of the jaws and in the development of the incisor teeth.

Nearly all rodents eat vegetable matter, and this calls for at least two kinds of teeth within the jaws. The rear teeth help consume the softer materials; the front teeth are highly specialized chisels that enable these mammals to tackle more difficult fibrous food and reduce it to edible shreds. The cutting incisors have only one enameled surface; the inner half of each incisor has a softer backing of dentine. As a rodent chews with these teeth, they are kept at an even length and are sharpened. They never stop growing during the animal's lifetime and do not have roots comparable to those of the other teeth.

Two orders of rodents are recognized, the distinction being based on the number of incisor teeth in the species. The largest order contains individuals having one pair of incisors in the upper and one pair in the lower jaw. The rabbit forms make up the second order, its members having two pairs of incisors in the upper jaw and one pair in the lower jaw.

The beavers are unique among mammals because of their well-organized home life and the unusual precautions they take to insure themselves of a winter food-supply. The mountain beaver of North America is perhaps the most primitive living rodent. It seems to be closely related to the fossil squirrel, Paramys, of Eocene times.

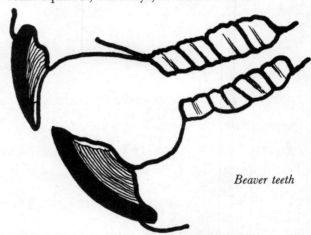

Beaver teeth

showing the typical rodent self-sharpening condition of the incisors

MAJOR GROUPINGS OF THE RODENTS

THE RODENTS

    Simplicidentata—order 1
        Sciuromorphs—suborder 1
            Squirrel, Gopher, Beaver, Others
        Myomorphs—suborder 2
            Jerboa, Vole, Mouse, Lemming, Rat, Others
        Hystricomorphs—suborder 3
            Porcupine, Capybara, Guinea pig, Agouti, Others

THE LAGOMORPHS

    Duplicidentata—order 2
        Pika, Rabbit, Hare, Others

CASTOROIDES, A GIANT BEAVER OF THE PLEISTOCENE

TOXODONT—*a primitive South American mammal*

Pronounced **tox . o . dont**

Translated, the name means "bow tooth."

The largest species were 10 feet long.

Flourished during Miocene times, 25 million years ago, but fossil records stretch from Paleocene times, 60 million years ago, to the Pleistocene, 1 million years ago.

All but a minute number of specimens have been found in South America.

Not generally displayed in the museums of this country.

THIS AWKWARD type of hoofed mammal is one of the reasons paleontologists look to South America for interesting discoveries. To date, the fossils of this southern continent are poorly known because many interesting deposits are probably blanketed under dense vegetation and tucked away in the vast unexplored land areas.

This is one of the many new fossil animals found by Charles Darwin on his historic voyage (1831–1836) in the *Beagle*. Darwin realized that on the basis of teeth alone this animal was unusual. Even to this day the toxodonts are a problem in classification.

The toxodonts were once very numerous. They varied in size from a few feet in length to giants ten feet long. In outward appearance these animals must have been crude and hairy. Most of them had heads out of proportion to their body size, and in a few species the skull bore short rhinoceros-like horns. In appearance the face of the animal was like that of a giant guinea pig. From species to species the skeleton varied in the region of the shoulders, and many species must have looked humpbacked. The entire body build was massive and, except for the face, the over-all appearance of the toxodonts was rhinoceros-like.

These animals flourished for better than thirty million years. They reached their greatest size in South America during the ice age, and practically all known specimens of this mammal come from South America. However, there are a few scattered specimens from Asia, and one from North America. All of these were found in Paleocene and Eocene rocks, and the animals represented seem to be forms ancestral to the South American species. So far there is no way to determine when and how they may have migrated into South America from Asia.

There are several related suborders of unusual mammals also best known from South America. Pyrotherium typifies one group of clumsy herbivorous forms whose evolution seems to have paralleled that of the toxodonts. Pyrotherium had an elephant-like snout that projected just beyond massive tusks in both the skull and lower jaws. Not many complete skeletons are known for any of these relatives of the toxodonts. Skulls and teeth are the principal discoveries.

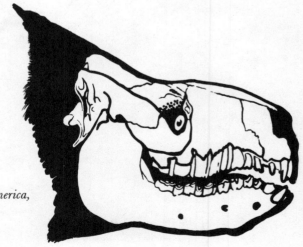

Skull of Nesodon, a Miocene toxodont of South America, length 16 inches

THREE TOXODONT SPECIES AND
A RELATED MAMMAL

Nesodon

These South American mammals were numerous and tremendously varied in size and facial appearance

Leontinia

Pyrotherium, related to toxodonts

Adinotherium

MACRAUCHENIA—*a strange South American mammal*

Pronounced **mack · raw · *keen* · ya**

Translated, the name means "great neck."
Was the size of a camel.
Lived during Pliocene and Pleistocene times, between 1 and 10 million years ago.
Found in South America.
Not displayed in this country.

MACRAUCHENIA is one of the unique South American mammals that did not migrate from that continent. The body and limbs of many closely related species suggest a camellike origin. The bones of the feet give the entire order the name Litopterna, which translated means "smooth-heeled."

Darwin discovered fossil remains of this animal while on the voyage of the *Beagle*. He could not have known that this species was the last of its line and the most highly developed. Within the order there are two main divisions between species. One family of litopterans is typified by Throatherium, an animal the size of a collie dog, whose feet bore a single horselike hoof. The more common second family had less specialized feet, bearing three toes and a thick pad of cartilage to walk upon.

The even teeth, long face, and location of the nostrils in the skull of Macrauchenia are a puzzle. Most authorities agree that the animal had a trunklike nose; others argue that the location of the nostrils means that the animal lived and fed in a swampy habitat. Recent studies tend to link the primitive hoofed mammal Phenacodus to these South American litopterans as their ancestor. There is no proof of this link; it is based merely on details of structure.

Judging by its teeth, this animal was both a browser and a grazer. The upper jaw bones are unusual because they are joined as a solid mass in front of the nose. Earlier forms were smaller and had longer face areas in the skull. As a general group the Litopterna seem to have been a South American counterpart of the horses of this country and Europe.

MACRAUCHENIA, A STRANGE BEAST FROM THE PLEISTOCENE OF SOUTH AMERICA

MEGATHERIUM—*a ground sloth of great size*

Pronounced **meg · a · *thee* · ree · um**

Translated, the name means "great beast."

These animals could rear up 18 or more feet from the ground. They were as large as an elephant.

Ground sloths flourished during Pliocene and Pleistocene times, from 10 million until 10 thousand years ago.

Fossils are found in Ohio, California, Florida, Kentucky, and many scattered localities throughout the United States.

Full skeletons are displayed at Ohio State University, the Los Angeles County Museum, the Denver Natural History Museum, and in several other large institutions.

THIS hairy beast is as typical of the ice age as the mammoths, mastodons, giant beavers, and other more familiar animals. Megatherium was the largest of the many ground sloths that existed from the Great Lakes to Patagonia, and from the Atlantic to the Pacific across the width of both North and South America. Sloth remains are fairly numerous, but the discoveries are scattered quite evenly across the entire country.

Though all of these and similar sloths are classed with the edentate (toothless) mammals, the ground sloths had several simple teeth in the rear of each jaw. The grinding surface of these teeth indicates that the animals must have lived primarily on leaves. The body structure of Megatherium shows that it spent a great deal of time feeding in a semi-erect position. The thick tail was probably used as a prop; the extremely large-boned hind feet must have acted as a stable base. The foot structure is interesting because the animal apparently shuffled along, using the outside edge of its foot instead of the full foot. This kind of gait led eventually to a reduction in the number of toes and the overdevelopment of the remaining ones. There was a thick pad on the side of each foot.

The tremendous size of Megatherium made him virtually invulnerable to attack from the numerous predators of the ice age. The animal's best protection from fierce animals like the saber-toothed cat was its powerful forearms and the gigantic single claw on each front foot. This claw was undoubtedly a tool in reaching for food; in some smaller species, the claws were an aid in digging for food.

Apparently all sloths were covered with long coarse hair. In addition, some had an extensive interlocking layer of bony plates to protect them further. It is not certain that all of these giant species had this kind of protection, but the tar pits of Rancho La Brea have produced so many of these bone ossicles that it seems likely. Though of elephant size, this sloth had a narrow body and head. The bony structure seems unnecessarily heavy for even a giant such as this.

The typical ground sloth of Miocene times was called Hapalops, which averaged four feet in total length. This small species gave rise to a rather common eight-foot species of Pleistocene times. As yet there can be no linking together of any of these sloths because of the scarcity of intermediate fossils that clearly bridge the gap between the better known types.

Ground sloths seem to have originated in South America, and it is on that continent that their skeletons are most numerous and diversified. The ground sloth is one of the few mammals that originated there. Living sloths continue to thrive in South America, but they do so as tree-dwelling forms. Ground sloths disappeared completely from all of their known territory late in the ice age. They fell victim to the same mysterious forces that wiped out the giants of other mammalian families.

MEGATHERIUM, A HAIRY BEAST, BIGGER THAN AN ELEPHANT

*Skull of Mylodon, a typical medium-sized ground sloth,
20 inches in length*

Skull of a glyptodont, 11 inches in length

GLYPTODONT—*an armored mammal*

Pronounced **glip · tow · dont**

Translated, the name means "grooved tooth."

There were many large and small species; the largest was 14 feet long and 5½ feet high.

Lived during Pliocene and Pleistocene times, 1 to 10 million years ago.

Found from the southern United States to Patagonia in South America.

Skeletons are poorly known; usually the carapace alone is displayed. Concrete and plaster of Paris replicas are a feature of many museums throughout the country.

THESE weird-looking animals are best known from fossil beds of South America. The remains of some species are found in the southern portions of the United States, principally in Texas.

Glyptodonts are related to armadillos, though the bony protective shield on top of their skulls, back, and tail is a great deal more solid than the platelike covering of the armadillos.

There must have been a considerable amount of coarse hair present on the entire body, particularly at the jointed places where the shell does not cover the soft skin of the animal.

The skull of this species is a massive, deep structure with a strange projection of bone below the eye. In spite of the term "edentate" (toothless), applied to this and other members of the family, glyptodonts had a few teeth, located in the rear portion of the jaws. They were simple enamelless structures more like pegs than teeth.

Classification of the entire group by the lack of teeth alone is not a valid distinction, for several other kinds of mammals are toothless, primarily due to the fact that they are anteaters and have no need for teeth.

In glyptodonts the vertebrae were fused into a solid mass at several points within the turtlelike shell that surrounded the body. In spite of the heavy armor some movement of these protected body portions was possible. The tail was entirely free-moving, though armored. In some species there was a clublike growth on the end of the tail, with knobs and spikes on it that must have afforded some protection to the animal. This club may also have been a sexual distinction.

The hind feet were strong and often bore blunt hoofs. The front legs and feet were not so stoutly built and in some cases bore strong claws that were used for digging. This animal may have occasionally walked on its hind legs as do living giant armadillos.

Glyptodonts superficially resemble some of the armored dinosaurs that existed until Late Cretaceous times. They are, however, true mammals in every sense of the word.

ORNITHORHYNCHUS—*the duck-billed platypus*

Pronounced **or · ni · tho · ring · kus**

Translated, the name means "bird beak."

Largest was 5 feet long; average nearer 2 feet long.

Fossils known only from Pleistocene deposits, 1 million years old.

Found in Australia.

Skeletons are not displayed in this country. Bones of the living species are shown in lieu of fossils.

THIS IS one of the most puzzling animals that ever lived. The duck-billed platypus and the echidna exist as an exclusive subclass among mammals. This is because they differ from all other mammals in that they lay eggs.

Both animals were once thought to be primitive ancestors of all mammals; this is no longer an accepted theory. At least one authority is willing to consider them remnants of a mammallike reptile line that developed in Mesozoic times and progressed slowly until the present.

Anatomists feel that the internal structure of the duck-billed platypus can give many answers to the puzzle that exists in properly placing the mammallike reptiles of the Permian Period.

Some of the obvious points that distinguish this animal are these: it has hair, webbed feet, no external ears, a soft bill, no teeth, a poisonous spur; it is aquatic, builds a nest, lays eggs, and carries the young in a pouch where it nurses them.

Internally, many parts of the skeleton are unique, but the most interesting portion is the region of the lower vertebrae and pelvis, where there are striking resemblances to the same structures in the mammallike reptiles of 150 million years ago. There is one great drawback to the intensive study of these interesting animals; so far there are no good fossil monotremes from any period but the Pleistocene.

As in the slightly related opossums, there was a wide variety of size among platypuses. One giant from Australia was five feet long.

GIANT KANGAROO—*a marsupial mammal*
Pronounced **kang · ga · *roo***

The name is of native Australian origin; marsupial means "having a pouch."

This animal was 10 feet tall.

Lived from Pleistocene times, less than 1 million years ago, to the very recent past.

Known only from Australia.

Not displayed in this country.

KANGAROOS probably evolved from tree-dwelling animals. In Australia today there are still some species that feed in low branches of trees.

Kangaroos represent one of the two large divisions among marsupial animals. These groupings are based on tooth structure and food habits, the larger number being insectivorous and carnivorous. The smaller division is herbivorous; this latter includes the kangaroo. The entire structure of these mammals is considered primitive. Their tremendous hind legs and muscular tail offer a grotesque appearance but provide a marvelous means of moving swiftly over open ground.

The fossil record of Australian mammals is so poorly known from any time prior to the ice age that it is difficult to discern any good reason why these animals should have developed the leaping habit so strongly.

A large modern kangaroo at rest stands five feet tall. From a sitting position it can leap twenty-five feet, and when it is in full speed it has been known to make leaps of forty feet. Giant fossil kangaroos stood at least eight or ten feet tall and must have been able to leap tremendous distances. Their hind legs indicate even stronger muscle structure than that found in modern forms.

Marsupials were once spread over the greater part of the world. They cannot be considered successful mammals, for outside Australia only the North and South American opossum survives.

The complete isolation of Australia protected the development of marsupials there. As a result, this pouched body plan is present in nearly all mammal types that live there.

This kangaroo was truly gigantic, but there is another giant marsupial known from Australia. It was a huge waddling animal with teeth like a rodent and appearance similar to the living wombat. Its name was Diprotodon; its skeleton indicates that it was fully twelve feet long.

ZEUGLODON—a whale

Pronounced **zoo · glow · don**

Translated, the name means "strap- or loop-toothed," because of the peculiar tooth structure.

Was 50 to 75 feet long.

Lived in Eocene times, 50 million years ago.

Found in marine deposits along the Atlantic coast.

A fine skeleton is in the Smithsonian Institution of Washington, D. C.; other large museums of the eastern United States exhibit this mammal.

THIS is a primitive whale. Its body was long, thin, and strong. The skull and jaws, though five or more feet long, bear great structural resemblance to those of the earliest flesh-eating mammals. The body structure, on the other hand, was considerably changed and even in Early Eocene times was quite like that of modern whales.

The forefeet had turned into steering paddles, but the hind legs and feet are scarcely seen in the skeleton and could not have protruded from the body. The high and narrow skull contained forty-four teeth, the full number for a primitive carnivore.

The nostrils of this whale had begun to shift backward in the skull and were located about midway from the point of the snout to the eyes. The mouth was not nearly so specialized as that of a modern whale. It is evident that this animal must have caught and consumed large fish, whereas most of today's big whales are in no way equipped for this kind of feeding but rely instead for the most part on a diet of minute organisms.

It is probable that the ancestors of whales were of house cat size. In the relatively short period of twenty million years they evolved from a four-footed land mammal to a completely aquatic existence.

There is no clear fossil evidence that bridges the gap between this kind of toothed whale and the two major types alive today in the oceans of the world. The complete skeletons of older whales are rare, though the skulls and teeth are found rather frequently in coastal areas. Judging by the speedy way a dead modern whale disintegrates after death, it is no wonder that the fossil record is sparse.

Most land-dwelling mammals evolved rather irregularly, being affected by the weather and many other factors that do not seem to have had nearly so harsh an effect on aquatic forms. Anatomical features in the body of the living whales show that these mammals have become steadily more refined in every detail for their life in the water.

Zeuglodon sometimes grew to be more than seventy feet in length. In life it must have looked very much like what we would call a sea serpent, spending considerable time on or near the surface. Porpoises, dolphins, narwhals, and today's toothed whales are all related to, though smaller than, this animal. The giant baleen (whalebone) whales are toothless, and their relationship to these creatures is not clear.

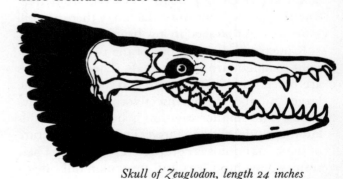

Skull of Zeuglodon, length 24 inches

Skeleton of Zeuglodon

ZEUGLODON, AN UNUSUAL PREDECESSOR OF MODERN WHALES

BLUE WHALE—*the largest mammal*

Scientific name: Balaenoptera. *Pronounced* **bay · lee · *nop* · ter · ra.** *Translated, the scientific name means "winged whalebone," because the sheets of whalebone in the jaws have a feathery look.*

Average size between 80 and 100 feet.

Lived from Pliocene times, 9 million years ago, until the present; still flourishing.

Found as fossils along continental coast lines. Very little of this animal is ever preserved as a fossil.

This kind of whale is not shown as a fossil. Living species typify the group, and these are usually seen in the largest museums in scale-model form.

As FAR as science knows, this is the largest animal that has ever lived on this earth. There are many estimates of the greatest length attained by this mammal, the longest authenticated record being 119 feet.

At present no one can state exactly when the whales began to adapt to a completely water-dwelling life. It is evident that they did branch off from the flesh-eating mammalian stock at least fifty to sixty million years ago.

The whale's skeleton and body are among the most remarkably complete adaptations away from a basic mammal stock. Whales are helpless when stranded on land, but in the water everything about their body organization becomes the epitome of efficiency. Whales are tremendously strong animals; they propel themselves through the water with a powerful up-and-down motion of their tails. This tail is intricately constructed of muscle and tendon that permit a flexibility of the tail shape as the animal maneuvers.

The blubber of a whale insulates the body and probably helps buoy it up in the water. During a deep dive, this fat layer may also absorb some of the pressure against the body. Whales have a tremendously large brain, even in relation to their great bulk. Every internal and external feature of the head illustrates some remarkable adaptation to aquatic life. Eyes are protected by a special secretion; the skull contains air sacs to help lift it to the surface. Nostrils have a special sealing system during dives, and the entire respiratory system provides for the split second intake of a vast amount of air and the gradual use of its oxygen over the period of a few minutes to an hour while the animal is under water.

Most species of whales have teeth; others have curtains of baleen through which they strain their minute invertebrate food. The blue whale is one of the latter toothless types. Examined in detail, these large whales become one of the most unusual mammals from any era of geologic time.

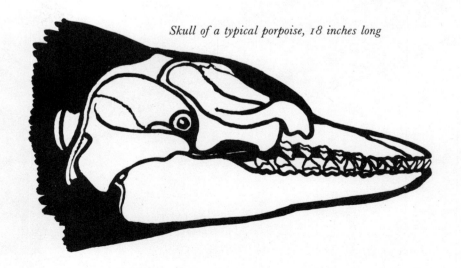

Skull of a typical porpoise, 18 inches long

THE BLUE WHALE, LARGEST ANIMAL THAT EVER LIVED

CONCLUSION

THE AGE OF MAMMALS is far from being over, but the fate of those species still flourishing on earth seems to lie in the hands of a fellow mammal, man.

It is almost impossible to predict what mammals will become in the future, for though men have studied fossils and living types diligently conclusions are remarkably difficult to achieve. This is mainly because of man's own upsetting influence on the balance of nature. It is also true because time works against the present generation of scholars. Even the most insignificant structural changes within a species take place over such long time periods that a single lifetime of careful observations can scarcely analyze them.

A few deductions are possible. These seem obvious unless some unforeseen act of nature—or of man—completely remakes our present world. Until that time, domesticated mammal species will continue to be bred to perfection for pleasure and utility. The many successful hoofed mammals and the rodents seem most likely to succeed for many centuries to come, but the future of rarer animals like the elephant, giraffe, wolf, whale, and others is far more doubtful.

As one thinks ahead to the time when zoos, game farms, and artificial propagation of species will be the only positive means of preserving certain mammals, the outlook is saddening. But there is this to consider: a prolonged and subtle change in climate or an ominous and growing hump in the earth's crust could gradually tip the balance of life in favor of a new ruling class on earth. Man's domination of the earth's mammalian fauna could become the shortest on record in the one billion five hundred million years since life first began on earth.

Unnoticed minor changes may be a prologue to our future.

All are mammals

BIBLIOGRAPHY

BOURLIÈRE, FRANÇOIS. *The Natural History of Mammals*. New York: Alfred A. Knopf, Inc., 1954.

BURT, WILLIAM H. *A Field Guide to the Mammals*. Boston: Houghton, Mifflin Co., 1952.

ELLENBERGER, W., BAUM, H., and DITTRICH, H. *An Atlas of Animal Anatomy for Artists*. New York: Dover Publications, Inc., 1949.

HOGBEN, LANCELOT. *From Cave Painting to Comic Strip*. New York: Chanticleer Press, Inc., 1949.

LEWINSOHN, RICHARD. *Animals, Men, and Myths*. New York: Harper and Brothers, 1954.

LUCAS, FREDERIC A. *Animals of the Past*. New York: American Museum Handbook Series, American Museum of Natural History, 1939.

LULL, RICHARD S. *Organic Evolution*. New York: The Macmillan Co., 1947.

MOORE, RUTH. *Man, Time, and Fossils*. New York: Alfred A. Knopf, Inc., 1953.

OSBORN, HENRY FAIRFIELD. *The Age of Mammals in Europe, Asia and North America*. New York: The Macmillan Co., 1921.

————. *The Origin and Evolution of Life*. New York: Charles Scribner's Sons, 1917.

RAPHAEL, MAX. *Prehistoric Cave Paintings*. New York: Pantheon Books, Inc., 1945.

ROMER, ALFRED S. *Vertebrate Paleontology*. Chicago: The University of Chicago Press, 1945.

SCHUCHERT, CHARLES, and DUNBAR, CARL O. *A Textbook of Geology: Part II, Historic Geology*. New York: John Wiley and Sons, Inc., 1941.

SCOTT, WILLIAM B. *A History of Land Mammals in the Western Hemisphere*. New York: The Macmillan Co., 1937.

SIMPSON, GEORGE GAYLORD. *Life of the Past*. New Haven: Yale University Press, 1953.

YOUNG, J. Z. *The Life of Vertebrates*. New York: Oxford University Press, 1952.

ZITTEL, KARL ALFRED VON. *Text-Book of Paleontology*, 3 vols. London: Macmillan and Co., 1900–1925.

BIBLIOGRAPHY FOR YOUNG PEOPLE

PARKER, BERTHA MORRIS. *Animals of Yesterday*.

PARKER, BERTHA MORRIS. *Life Through the Ages*.

PARKER, BERTHA MORRIS. *Stories Read From the Rocks*. These three small volumes are part of a basic science education series published by Row, Peterson and Co., Evanston, Illinois. They are graded very carefully to fit a specific need in the elementary age level. Most museums sell the series.

BAITY, ELIZABETH CHESLEY. *America Before Man*. New York: The Viking Press, 1953.

KNIGHT, CHARLES R. *Life Through the Ages*. New York: Alfred A. Knopf, Inc., 1946.

REED, W. MAXWELL, and LUCAS, JANNETTE M. *Animals on the March*. New York: Harcourt, Brace, and Co., 1937.

REED, W. MAXWELL. *The Earth for Sam*. New York: Harcourt, Brace, and Co., 1930.

Numerous annals, bulletins, and special publications were used, especially those printed by:

> The American Museum of Natural History, New York
> The Carnegie Institution of Washington, D. C.
> The Carnegie Institution of Pittsburgh, Pennsylvania
> The Los Angeles County Museum
> The Denver Natural History Museum
> The Smithsonian Institution of Washington, D. C.

Many magazine articles were source material; most were from:

> *Natural History* magazine, printed by the American Museum of Natural History
> *Scientific American* magazine, printed by Scientific American, Inc.

About the Author

WILLIAM E. SCHEELE, director of the Cleveland Museum of Natural History, was born in Cleveland in 1920. He won scholarships in art and biology and was graduated from the Cleveland School of Art and Western Reserve University in 1947. While a student at the art school in 1939, he won the first annual Bird Art Contest, sponsored by the Cleveland Museum of Natural History, and very shortly thereafter became a member of their staff.

Army service from 1942 to 1946 interrupted his career and took him through all of England and into five countries on the continent of Europe. Immediately after his discharge from the armed forces, he returned to Western Reserve University and the museum. Upon graduation in June, 1947, he became Chief of Preparation and Exhibition. In 1949 he was appointed director of the museum and was at that time the youngest museum director in the country.

Mr. Scheele's work in revising exhibits and presenting museum material in a clear and colorful manner brought to his attention the need of a book about fossils and prehistoric animals that was accurate enough to please a scientist as well as being inviting and helpful to the less advanced reader. His purpose was to do a book which would supply information in fact and picture in the most readable, accurate fashion possible. The result was *Prehistoric Animals,* probably one of the most lavishly illustrated books on the subject. In *The First Mammals,* he uses the same principle of blending text and illustration to depict the further development of animal life during the past sixty million years, the period of mammalian supremacy.

His outside activities include painting natural-history subjects (he has exhibited in many museums), gem cutting, and fossil hunting. All of his non-working hours are spent with his wife and three sons on their tree farm near Chardon, Ohio.